THE TURN OF
A CENTURY
1885-1910

THE TURN OF A CENTURY
1885-1910

Art Nouveau ~ Jugendstil Books

Department of Printing
and Graphic Arts
The Houghton Library
Harvard University
1970

Upper cover
William Brown MacDougall. Half-title for *Isabella or the Pot of Basil*. 1898 (Cat. No. 40)

Lower cover
Charles Ricketts. Vale Press monogram for *Early Poems*. 1896 (Cat. No. 12)

End Papers
Emil Rudolf Weiss. *Gugeline*. *1899* (Cat. No. 100)

Introduction

RT NOUVEAU is a decorative art, especially as it pertains to book illustration and design. It is a rhythmic surface movement with line and pattern often building up a nervous intensity within a closed graphic space; one hears of the "leitmotiv of the sinuous curve," the "tortured arabesque," the "whiplash," or as S. Tschudi Madsen defined its principal ornamental characteristic, "the asymmetrically undulating line terminating in a whiplike energy-laden movement." The last decade of the Nineties has carried with it the stigma of *fin de siècle, décadence,* a *Weltschmerz* denoting a decline of vigor. The strongest contributing factors to this mood and philosophy were, first, the Symbolist Movement in literature, which Arthur Symons in 1893 described as "a new and beautiful and interesting disease," and second, the Aesthetic Movement in England culminating in Art Nouveau, which Walter Crane branded in 1911 as "that strange decorative disease."

If indeed art and society were in a sickly state during the period 1885 to 1910, one should not misrepresent the facts, and certainly not be blinded to its tonic qualities in bookmaking and book design. Today, Art Nouveau needs less justification since after two generations of repudiation it is back in fashion — to paraphrase Whistler's *Ten O'Clock:* Art [Nouveau] is [again] upon the Town!

It was a period bursting with creative energy and imagination and an intensified striving for new and "modern" forms of stylistic expression, an unshackling of the heavy and cloying drapery of Victorian design and the inorganic *appliqué* of the Industrial Revolution.

William Morris was the platform from which modern book design started. While never a conscious participant in Art Nouveau, and indeed standing apart, Morris' championing of the Arts and Crafts movement and his belief in the equality and fraternity of the arts culminated in the high standard of craftsmanship of the Kelmscott Press. He proclaimed a return to the medieval craft system — the source of true Socialism — when the designer and craftsman were one. Walter Crane expressed Morris' philosophy when he wrote of the medieval craftsman in an essay in *The Claims of Decorative Art* : "Ornament was organic, completely adapted to its material, and expressive of its object . . . the production of all things for the service or delight of man for *use* instead of, as now, for *profit,* the craftsman was an artist, and all objects under his hand naturally developed a characteristic beauty."

We accept the Nineties as a renascent period, despite its many extravagances and high jinks, a period of mental activity and quickening imagination, a period when the quality of living and environment was under scrutiny, a period of not only art-for-art's-sake, but art-for-life's-sake, a *belle époque,* but nonetheless compounded with a certain malaise, a feverish restlessness and confused heterodoxy. Among that intellectual and cultural elite, the *arbiter elegantiarum* of the age, the dominant concern was mode of life, or "life style," as we say today. Arthur Symons, an ardent advocate of the taste of the times, put it this way : "Art begins when a man wishes to immortalize the most vivid moment he has ever lived. Life has already, to one not an artist, become art in that moment. And the making of one's life into art is after all the first duty and privilege of every man."

The artists, writers, poets, publishers and editors

in England involved in the renascent Nineties were a pride of lions: James McNeill Whistler, Oscar Wilde, Aubrey Beardsley, John Lane, Charles Ricketts, Charles Shannon, Arthur Symons, Gleeson White, Herbert Horne, Selwyn Image, Laurence Housman, John Gray, William Rothenstein, Laurence Binyon, Max Beerbohm, and Algernon Swinburne. They were a remarkably spirited, cultivated, enlightened and urbane group, many of them fresh down from Oxford, with a will to dazzle the world with their wit, wisdom and winsome ways. However languid their exterior posture, they all burned inwardly with that "hard gem-like flame" prescribed by Walter Pater, and mused upon the "finer shades" of their spiritual and mortal souls. Their versatility was prodigious. Ricketts was a painter, draughtsman, engraver, stage designer, critic, essayist, belle-lettrist, and a collector-connoisseur of sufficient prestige to have been offered the directorship of the National Gallery during World World I, which he turned down. He bequeathed his and Shannon's art collection to a grateful nation. We think of Laurence Binyon as a distinguished curator and Orientalist at the British Museum, but he wrote poems well enough for Wilde to address him in print as a "young singer," while he designed and cut a woodblock frontispiece worthy of Lucien Pissaro's Eragny Press. All of these lions wrote articulate and clever memoirs about themselves and their clever friends.

Oscar Wilde was unquestionably the master of the first phase of Art Nouveau, its most vivid and eloquent spokesman, its most impassioned apostle. Already in the Eighties he had charmed London by his remark about living up to his blue-and-white china. He was the proclaimed aesthetician. Even in fashion and dress the response was rapturous: "... slim ladies with a tendency towards mysticism preferred the dress of the Middle Ages; *Belles Dames Sans Merci* and *Demoiselles Elues* materialized in Chelsea, and descended upon Piccadilly ... 'What will Oscar think?' was the question they pondered after having rigged themselves out in peacock feathers as an up-to-date version of Psyche." (Jullian).

Aubrey Beardsley was the *enfant terrible* who "crowded the vision of the period" with his stunning black and white. His *Morte Darthur,* appearing in half-crown monthly parts beginning June 1893, was a tour de force. Those who saw it in the guise of the Kelmscott tradition were astonished by his powerful handling of black masses and quick to note the strange new stylization of forms and ornament unacceptable to the Pre-Raphaelite formulas of Morris and Burne-Jones. Joseph Pennell in *The Studio* praised the distinctive quality of Beardsley's pen line, and the fidelity of reproduction by the process-engraving woodblock method. Oscar Wilde exclaimed "all art is at once surface and symbol." Then appeared *The Yellow Book* with Beardsley as art editor, its shocking yellow cover a sensation and delight. Overnight the whole world turned yellow. Combined with Beardsley's own black and white illustrations and the modern prose fancy of new young authors, *The Yellow Book* became the byword of a bizarre and outrageous modernity.

With the *Salome* in 1894 one becomes acutely aware of Beardsley's brilliant and sardonic powers in illustration: "No one ever carried a simple line to its inevitable end with such sureness and firmness of purpose," Robert Ross observed. If his subjects appeared to one critic sinister and artificial, Beardsley could rejoin: "I draw folk as I see them. Surely, it is not my fault that they fall into certain lines and angles." Holbrook Jackson called Beardsley's pictures "hot house growths" of thought, concluding that he was "essentially a decorator; but with the perversity of one phase of his generation he made decoration a thing in itself." Notwithstanding, as a decorator Beardsley continues to crowd our vision as the all-pervasive essence of Art Nouveau.

Whistler's *The Gentle Art of Making Enemies,* which appeared in 1890 at the turn of the decade, is by contrast a masterpiece of understatement, with the elusive refinement of Japanese design, illustrated sparingly with delicate pen line drawings of the famous butterfly *remarque.* Every detail of design and typography came under the fastidious scrutiny of the artist. Whistler was not concerned merely with the selection of the textual material, but also with the impression it should make. Every morning at eleven he would swoop down upon his publisher Heinemann and carry him off to the Savoy for lunch. There on the balcony overlooking the Embankment they would review the page by page layout. "Hours were spent often in the 'arranging' of a single Butterfly, each of which he designed especially to convey a special meaning. They danced, laughed, mocked, stung, defied, triumphed, drooped wings over the farthing damages, spread them to fly across the Channel, and expressed every word and almost every thought. He designed the title-page; a design contrary to all established rules, but with the charm, the balance, the harmony, the touch of personality he gave to everything...." (Pennell). The binding, half yellow-ochre cloth spine with reverse-snob brown wrapping-paper sides as plain background for the glittering butterfly, was the utmost in elegant simplicity and restraint. It became the standard binding for all subsequent books of Whistler's authorship, for example, *The Baronet and the Butterfly*.

Whistler's prose, like his art, was in consummate taste and glowed with pale lustre, as in this polished phrase from his *Ten O'Clock*:

"In the citron wing of the pale butterfly, with its dainty spots of orange, he sees before him the stately halls of fair gold, with their slender saffron pillars, and is taught how the delicate drawing high upon the walls shall be traced in tender tones of orpiment, and repeated by the base in notes of graver hue...."

Charles Ricketts is Beardsley's rival in the winnowing judgment of time. His graphic style was equally eclectic, following Pre-Raphaelite models, but more purely linear, more lyrical, basically grounded on Renaissance prototypes like the fine line woodcuts of the *Hypnerotomachia Poliphili*. He and Shannon, his lifetime partner, were, like Morris, thoroughly schooled in the technical aspects of printing and printing reproduction, and they founded the Vale Press together. Unlike Beardsley, who saw his art in terms of isolated illustrations to be inserted between the text pages of a book, Ricketts conceived the book from inside out as the harmonious interplay of page, text, illustration, ornament and binding. To some critics *The Sphinx* is Ricketts' finest achievement, selected as he was by Wilde as illustrator and designer. Intellectually and artistically these two collaborators worked in harmonious correspondence, and the luxurious imagery of Wilde's masterpiece of epicurean poetry infuses its strange and exotic emotion on the stately and impressive line of Ricketts' symbolic designs, decorated throughout in red, green and black and bound with a beautiful design gilt-stamped on ivory vellum. One illustration portrays a lovely group of maidens clustering round "the moon-horned Io" as she weeps. But the *Melancholia* drawing for the frontispiece with its passionate, bittersweet, intricate mystery and rhythmic arabesque is the quintessence of Art Nouveau refinement and elegance.

Decadence in its stylistic sense was a prevalent influence in Art Nouveau. In literature it is compared to the decline of the Greek and Latin periods: "an intense self-consciousness, a restless curiosity in research, an over-subtilizing refinement upon refinement, a spiritual and moral perversity." (Holbrook Jackson). In England an influence came from the Pre-Raphaelite Brotherhood, but particularly from Dante Gabriel Rossetti and Swinburne. Principally, the modern decadence in England was an echo of the French movement which began with Gautier, Verlaine and Huysmans. French decadence began with *Mademoiselle de Maupin* and ended with Huysmans' *A Rebours*. English decadence began with Pater's studies in art and poetry, *The Renaissance*, and ended with Wilde's *Picture of Dorian Gray* and Beardsley's *Under the Hill*. Hand in hand with decadence was the revolt against rationalism and a revival of mysticism, which revealed itself in the Theosophical and Rosicrucian movements, in the popularity of Maeterlinck, and in the numerous conversions to Rome.

In literature it was the search for purple passages which satisfied the call of the hour, the suggestive ardor of Rossetti's poems with their "vagueness and utterness," to use an expression applied to Verlaine by George Moore. Preference for the artificial over the natural prevailed. When a reviewer attacked Arthur Symons' early poems as "unwholesome" because he said they had "a faint smell of patchouli about them," Symons flew to their defense: "Patchouli! Well, why not Patchouli? Is there any reason in nature why we should write exclusively about the natural blush, if the delicately acquired blush of rouge has any attraction for us?"

3

The attitudinizing of the aesthetes inevitably produced effete excesses. Preciosity of presentation was one manifestation centering around the Wilde circle. Commenting on a little book of poems, *Rose Leaf and Apple Leaf* by Rennell Rodd with an introduction by Oscar Wilde, published in 1882, Walter Hamilton gushed: "A dainty little volume of poems clothed in most exquisite attire. The printed matter occupies one side only of a thin transparent sheet of hand-made parchment paper, interleaved with pale apple green, the delicate tint of which shows through the printed page in a manner most grateful to the reader's eye. The illustrations are of a decidedly Japanese type and the outer case is of white vellum...." Ada Leverson's memoir, *The Importance of Being Oscar,* satirizes this trend:

"... margin in every sense was in demand, and I remember looking at the poems of John Gray (considered the incomparable poet of the age) and when I saw the tiniest rivulet of text meandering through the very large meadow of margin, I suggested to Oscar Wilde that he should publish a book, *all* margin, full of beautiful unwritten thoughts, and have this blank volume bound in some Nile-green skin powdered with gilt Nenuphars and smoothed with hard ivory, decorated with gold by Ricketts, if not Shannon, and printed on Japanese paper, and each volume must be a collector's piece, a numbered one of a limited 'first' (and last) edition; 'very rare.' He approved and suggested 'It should be dedicated to you, and the unwritten text illustrated by Aubrey Beardsley. There must be five hundred signed copies for particular friends, six for the general public and one for America.'"

As a general characteristic one may say that book decoration in English Art Nouveau was substantially based on organic plant forms, but always contained within well-defined linear borders in the more or less conservative Kelmscott tradition. John Russell Taylor makes a distinction between English and Continental style: "British art nouveau is a reaction in favour of spareness and simplicity after the intricacy of what had gone before, while Continental art noveau is a further elaboration. Continental art nouveau is largely based on the much-discussed sinuous line, the bulging, bulbous, willfully irregular shape, while British art nouveau is more a matter of flat or slightly curved surfaces, straight or slightly curved lines. British art nouveau is concerned with the arrangement of empty spaces, Continental with their filling."

The Belle Epoque was the age of the Eternal Feminine when the Parisian scene was dominated by the reigning queens of stage, music hall and Montmartre café: Sarah Bernhardt, Réjane, Loie Fuller, Cléo de Mérode, Yvette Guilbert, Jane Avril and La Goulue, while the grand horizontals, "Les Trois Grands" — Emilienne d'Alençon, Liane de Pougy and Caroline Otéro — ruled the other side of the proscenium. It is significant that the leading Art Nouveau artists involved in design and book decoration in the Nineties hung their fame on the protagonists of the stage and entertainment world: Eugène Grasset, Georges de Feure, Alphonse Mucha and Toulouse-Lautrec. Grasset was Swiss, de Feure of Dutch and Belgian descent, and Mucha Czech.

The period 1890-1900 was intensively active in the decorative arts in France, and the name "Art Nouveau" derives from Samuel Bing's shop opened in 1895. The term in its contemporary application referred exclusively to French decorative arts. In 1898 the German critic Julius Meier-Graefe opened his shop in Paris, "La Maison Moderne" with the purpose of providing somewhat less expensive products of the new art. He chose one of Grasset's new typefaces for the shop's publications.

When Eugène Grasset first came to Paris he was helped by the photographer Gillot, for whom he designed furniture, and Rodolphe de Salis, for whom he designed some culs-de-lampes of cat heads for the periodical *Chat Noir.* It was Gillot in 1893 who commissioned him to illustrate *Histoire des Quatres Fils Aymon,* the first French illustrated book to present a mise-en-page fusing illustration and text. The book was indifferently received until Octave Uzanne praised it in an article in *Le Livre.* Grasset made a poster for Sarah Bernhardt's *Jeanne d'Arc,* but the thick "stained glass" outlines were rather too static to flatter the flamboyant tastes of the actress. Bernhardt turned to Alphonse Mucha after he had pleased her with his poster design for *Gismonda.* Thereafter he executed most of the posters for the Théâtre de la Renaissance, *La Dame aux Camélias, Lorenzaccio* and *Medée,* and from 1898 those for the Théâtre Sarah Bernhardt, *Théodora, La Tosca* and *Hamlet.* For many of her performances Mucha designed settings and costumes.

The eventual success of Grasset's early book led to the appearance of other books similarly designed. Carlos Schwabe illustrated Baudelaire's *Les Fleurs du Mal* with colored etchings and made a series of illustrations for *L'Evangile de l'enfance de notre Seigneur Jésus-Christ*; Georges de Feure illustrated Zola's *Le Rêve*; Gaston de Latenay, the tale of *Nausikaa*; Boutet de Monval, *Nos Enfants* and *Chansons de France*; and Alphonse Mucha, *Ilsée, Princesse de Tripoli.* This last was Mucha's chef-d'oeuvre in the field of book design, a lavish production on which the publisher Piazza spared no pains. The title-page is effectively graceful with the cameo head of the princess enframed by a delicate interlace in the shape of a horseshoe arch.

Maurice Denis exceeds his talent as a painter in his designs for Gide's *Le Voyage d'Urien* and Verlaine's *Sagesse.* His cover lithograph for Debussy's *La damoiselle élue,* based on Rossetti's *The Blessed Damozel,* unites the "lovely strangeness" of Denis' style with the two other masters. This points the way to Walter Pater's theory that "all art constantly aspires towards the condition of music," and that the perfection of lyrical poetry depends "on a certain suppression or vagueness of mere subject so that the definite meaning almost expires." Beauty, therefore, is the sensuous manifestation of an idea, the spiritual element.

In Belgium book decoration in the early stages of this period was dominated by Henry van de Velde and Théo van Rysselberghe. The books tended to be of simple quarto or octavo format and and often conservative in typography. The several books published in Brussels with frontispieces by Redon offer little to the advance of book design. Van de Velde, a man of immense talent and versatility as designer and architect, expressed due admiration for Ruskin, Morris and the English school in an article on "English Wallpaper" in *L'Art Moderne,* 1893. He remarked that Walter Crane triumphed over all the others by virtue of "the rhythmic vegetation in his designs and *les* *lignes de très spéciale souplesse."* In decoration, however, van de Velde's designs went far beyond his English peers; they were generally vignette ornaments of a strong abstract character, with the bulbous cartouche style one associates with sixteenth-century German or Dutch mannerist engraving known variously as *Knorpelwerk* (cartilage style) or *Ohrmuschelstil* (shell or ear muscle style). Occasionally the terms *Schnörkelstil* (flourish style) or *Bandwurmstil* (tapeworm style) were applied to designate this style of the Nineties. In Germany it was often called *Belgische* or *Veldesche* after van de Velde. On his removal to Germany, he decorated two books of prime importance in the annals of Art Nouveau design, published by Insel-Verlag, both by Nietzsche: *Also sprach Zarathustra* (1908) and *Ecce Homo* (1908). The format becomes strong and imposing, the designs with rich intricate arabesques, like mosaic tiles, in unusual virile colors of reddish-purple or chocolate. *Zarathustra* is enriched with gold printing in which the Germans and Austrians excelled. Van Rysselberghe's ornament was conservatively restrained but with a high degree of light and imaginative elegance.

In Holland significant Art Nouveau book design was used principally for decoration on hard or soft covers of trade bindings, many of which were extraordinarily effective, even when the interior designs remained conservatively unaffected. Some of this revival of the arts of the book was due to K. Groesbeek, director of the publishing firm of Scheltema and Holkema, and of the art shop Van Wisselingh, who rallied many of the Amsterdam artists and designers. One of the most original book designs was that of G. W. Dijsselhof for a Dutch translation of Walter Crane's *The Claims of Decorative Art.* In this case, and many others, Indonesian batik patterns were frequently adapted as motifs for these designs.

One of the principal outlets for the dissemination of modern art, design, literature and the new critical and aesthetic point of view were the periodicals which sprang up all over Europe and America and quickly became a source of international exchange. One of the earliest was the Century Guild *Hobby Horse* (1884, 1886-1892, 1893-1894) edited by Arthur Heygate Macmurdo and

5

Herbert P. Horne. In book design we associate Macmurdo with his woodcut title-page for *Wren's City Churches* (1883), a strikingly abstract example of proto-Art Nouveau. Macmurdo and Selwyn Image, a pupil of Ruskin, were the founders of the Century Guild, the first Art Nouveau arts and crafts movement. The *Hobby Horse* maintained a high literary standard and made a conscious effort to practice in content and form its preachings of good design — printed on good paper with careful layout and fresh decorative woodcut ornaments. Similar efforts in England were *The Dial* (1889-1897), an "occasional publication" edited by Charles Shannon and Charles Ricketts; *The Yellow Book* (1894-1897); *The Savoy* (1896). In Berlin there were *Pan* (1895-1900) and *Die Insel* (1899-1902); in Munich, *Jugend* (1896-1933), the magazine that gave the Jugendstil its name; in Vienna, *Ver Sacrum* (1898-1903). These are merely the leading periodicals with broad international influence which made some claim to good design; many more existed of varying character. For example, *The Studio* was an influential outlet for the arts, particularly arts and crafts, but except for its cover made no pretense to distinctive design.

A phenomenon of an eclectic style like Art Nouveau is the difficulty of succinctly defining its formal characteristics without running into contradictions. We no sooner move across Europe to Germany and Austria than we discover what appears to be a developing countermovement away from the basic principle of the sinuous curve, undulating rhythm and enclosed outline. Implicit in this countermovement was a retraction from the natural forms of nature towards tectonic forms and more abstract expression, moving finally to the repudiation of ornament altogether.

In Germany Jugendstil was a diversity of floral and abstract tendencies, which towards 1900 built up a certain tense polarization. In reality, the two developed in successive overlapping stages. Before 1900 the inspiration was principally floral; after 1900 almost exclusively abstract. Floral Jugendstil was mainly found in the ornamentation of small objects in the applied arts, and in book decoration. It has been described as "light, delicate, sensitively shaped, often buoyant or spindly, sometimes confused." (Schmutzler). There is a spring-like atmosphere ranging from fairy tale to fantastic in which symbolism often plays a part, or else an ardently Romantic approach to nature. It is curious that in a culture that had developed the highest Rococo tradition the *rocaille* element was rare in Jugendstil. The late abstract phase of German Jugendstil was largely inspired by van de Velde, who had moved to Weimar in 1901. Structural elements entered into design which showed the primacy of architectural discipline. We remember this tendency in English Art Nouveau: Herbert Horne, C. R. Ashbee, and C. R. Mackintosh were architects; Beardsley, Talwin Morris, Anning Bell all had draughting experience or at some point worked in an architect's office.

Munich was the center of German Jugendstil, the Munich group comprising Peter Behrens, August Endell, Otto Eckmann, Richard Riemerschmid, Herman Obrist, Bernhard Pankok and Bruno Paul. Of these seven, Eckmann and Behrens were the most important for graphic design and book ornament. It was in *Pan* and *Jugend* and *Ver Sacrum* that the young German and Austrian designers and architects published their first Jugendstil ornament. Otto Eckmann was the leader of floral Jugendstil, and his vignettes in the early issues of *Pan* are among the most inventive of the period, a synthesis of crisp, graceful, chiseled, contained, stylized ornament; some showing a knowledge of Japanese sword guards, others abstracted to a few powerful calligraphic symbols of entwined, swelling and contracting lines. Side by side with Eckmann, *Pan* published some fine decorative borders by Thomas Theodor Heine and Emil Rudolf Weiss.

In 1897 the Vienna Secession group was founded with Gustav Klimt as the moving spirit. Among the founders were the architects Josef Hoffmann and Joseph Maria Olbrich. Floral Art Nouveau hardly existed in Austria — the Secession style was geometrically inspired, a compound of rectangles, squares and circles, additively and two-dimensionally applied. This Austrian countermovement had its parallel in the Glasgow School, the work of "The Four," the Scottish architect Charles Rennie Mackintosh, Herbert MacNair and Margaret and Frances Macdonald. The "Four Macs" were invited to exhibit at the Vienna Secession in 1900, and their

6

extraordinary originality was recognized abroad while remaining comparatively unknown in their native country.

Ver Sacrum, the most elegantly designed of all the periodicals, was the organ of the Vienna Secession and became the outlet for Klimt and his group, displaying some fine black and white vignettes by Hoffmann and Olbrich. Hoffmann cultivated the square, while Olbrich cultivated the circle. In the layout of *Ver Sacrum* one follows the evolution in design of "parallel, non-rhythmic repetition of similar elements" which were basic to its form-language.

The influence of Klimt was evident in the Viennese graphic work and book decoration. The illustrations for children's books by Czeschka, Heinrich Lefler and Joseph Urban with their glittering fantasy and flat mosaic-like friezes, printed in brilliant colors with rich use of gold, show the impact of Klimt's majestic style.

In 1903, together with Koloman Moser and C. O. Czeschka, Hoffmann founded the Wiener Werkstätte, an arts and crafts movement which in design principle widened the gap with Art Nouveau. The programs for the *Theater und Kabarett Fledermaus* (1907) and Kokoschka's *Die Traeumenden Knaben* (1908) were forward-moving products of the Wiener Werkstätte which spelled the fading vestiges of the Jugendstil movement, opening the way to twentieth century Expressionism and Cubism.

Art Nouveau reached its peak at the Turin exhibition of 1902. Its vocabulary continued in use throughout the first decade of the new century and lingered on until the first World War. Although the attitudes it represented were not congenial to those years of chaos, the experiments in expressive line, distortion, and abstraction of the Art Nouveau-Jugendstil years were sources of vitality in the first quarter of the new century.

Peter A. Wick

The first comprehensive exhibition of Art Nouveau books was held at the Grolier Club in December 1968, organized by the former Librarian Gabriel Austin. I am indebted to him for his advice and for the valuable groundwork the Grolier laid for this Houghton exhibition, in which the selection is frequently duplicated.

To my collaborators, Eleanor M. Garvey, Associate Curator in the Department of Printing and Graphic Arts, and Mrs. Anne Blake Smith, a former colleague, who prepared the catalogue entries; to Mrs. Karen Rogers and Anne Donaldson for typing and research in bibliography, my thanks and obligation. And to Larry Webster of Thomas Todd Company, who designed this catalogue, my appreciation.

I am grateful for the advice and assistance from many sources: Dr. Wilhelm Mrazek, Director of the Österreichisches Museum für Angewandte Kunst, Vienna; Messrs. Christian M. Nebehay and John Sailer, Vienna; Mr. Lucien Goldschmidt, New York; Dr. Eduard Sekler, Director of the Carpenter Center for Visual Arts, Harvard University; Dr. Thomas Howarth Dean of the Faculty of Architecture, University of Toronto.

To the lenders my special thanks: Mr. Raphael Esmerian, Mr. David Godine, Dr. Thomas Howarth, Mrs. Donald F. Hyde, Mr. Jonathan Joseph, Mr. and Mrs. John McAndrew, Mr. John D. Merriam, Mrs. Lillian Nassau, and Mr. and Mrs. Harborne Stuart.

To my colleagues, appreciation for loans and assistance: Miss Agnes Mongan, Director and Curator of Drawings, Fogg Museum of Art; Dr. Wolfgang Freitag, Librarian, Fogg Art Library; Mr. John David Farmer, Curator of the Busch-Reisinger Museum; Mr. Perry T. Rathbone, Director, Miss Eleanor A. Sayre, Curator of Prints, and Mr. Clifford S. Ackley, Assistant Curator, Museum of Fine Arts, Boston.

ENGLAND

All art is at once surface and symbol.

There is a danger of modern book illustration becoming too pictorial. What we need is good book-ornament — decorative ornament that will go with type and printing, and give to each page a harmony and unity of effect.

Oscar Wilde

. . . to fix the last fine shade, the quintessence of things; to fix it fleetingly; to be a disembodied voice, and yet the voice of a human soul; that is the ideal of Decadence.

Arthur Symons

1

Walter Crane, *The Sirens Three*
Walter Crane, designer and illustrator
Dedicated to William Morris
London, Macmillan and Company, 1886

Decorated title-page, half-title, 41 decorated pages with illustrations and hand-lettered text, vignettes, and ornaments by Walter Crane. Printed by Richard Clay and Sons.

First copy: 10⅞ x 8¼ in. Original gray boards, upper cover with title and design of sirens in darker grays by Crane, lower cover with Macmillan device, gray end papers with curvilinear design in chalk-white by Crane. Presentation copy, with inscription from Walter Crane to William Morris, with autograph copy of Crane's dedication sonnet and Morris' letter of thanks.

Caroline Miller Parker collection of Walter Crane, Gift of A. H. Parker

Second copy: 10⅞ x 8¼ in. Bound like first copy. Caroline Miller Parker collection of Walter Crane, Gift of A. H. Parker

Although Walter Crane disclaimed any connection with Art Nouveau, his early work forms a prelude to the new style, and he influenced some of its developments, especially on the Continent. Trained as a wood-engraver, he designed numerous children's books, cards, and even wallpaper, for he was closely associated with the Arts and Crafts movement. He was influenced by the Pre-Raphaelites, by the Japanese, and also by William Blake, whose engraved books are direct ancestors of *The Sirens Three,* designed with the same careful integration of text and illustration.

Ref: Aslin, *The Aesthetic Movement,* p. 160-162; Taylor, *The Art Nouveau Book,* p. 64-66; Hofstätter, *Jugendstil Druckkunst,* p. 86-87; Konody, *Walter Crane,* p. 60, 61, 63 ill.; Massé, *A Bibliography of Walter Crane,* p. 36; Crane, *The Decorative Illustration of Books,* p. 174 ill.

1a
Walter Crane, *The Sirens Three*
28 drawings. 1886

Pen and ink, heightened with Chinese white.
9⅝ x 6⅝ in.

Caroline Miller Parker collection of Walter Crane, Gift of A. H. Parker

2

Edmund Spenser, *The Shepheard's Calender*
Walter Crane, designer and illustrator
London and New York, Harper and Brothers, 1898

Decorated double title-page, borders and initials by Walter Crane, the illustrations signed with device of crane with initials *WC.* Printed by the Chiswick Press.

8 x 6⅜ in. Original green cloth, upper cover gilt-stamped with title and multi-color design of piping shepherd by Crane, signed with device of crane with initials *WC*; lower cover gilt-stamped with signs of zodiac and multi-color design of tree with sheep and shepherd's crook by Crane, signed with device of crane with initials *WC*; spine with title on banner attached to shepherd's crook. Green and white figured end papers with design of reeds and medallions of Pan and nymph by Crane.

Caroline Miller Parker collection of Walter Crane, Gift of A. H. Parker

Crane was associated with William Morris in the first Kelmscott book, *The Story of the Glittering Plain,* of 1891. The pictorial woodcuts and foliated borders of *The Shepheard's Calendar* suggest the same interest in Medieval and Renaissance art. Crane's personal device, on the other hand, composed of a crane with his initials *WC,* is Japanese in origin, like the marks of Whistler and Beardsley. Crane was a theorist, as well as a practitioner of the arts, and his books included *The Claims of Decorative Art* (1892), *Of the Decorative Illustration of Books* (1896), and *Ideals in Art* (1905).

Ref: Aslin, *The Aesthetic Movement,* p. 160-162; Taylor, *The Art Nouveau Book,* p. 64-66; Hofstätter, *Jugendstil Druckkunst,* p. 86-87; Konody, *Walter Crane,* p. 75-78 ill.; Massé, *A Bibliography of Walter Crane,* p. 51.

3

James Abbott McNeill Whistler, *The Gentle Art of Making Enemies*
James Abbott McNeill Whistler, designer
London, William Heinemann, 1890

Unillustrated. Frequent decorative use of Whistler's butterfly device. Printed by the Ballantyne Press.

9¼ x 7⅜ in. Large paper copy. Brown wrappers, gilt-stamped with title and Whistler's butterfly device, top edges gilt.

Apparently one of the special copies prepared for private distribution by Whistler, without the leaf giving the number of copies in the regular large paper edition. Large paper edition of 250 copies (150 for England, 100 for America). The regular large paper copies and the small paper copies, 8 x 6¼ in., were bound in half ochre cloth with brown boards gilt-stamped with the title and butterfly device.

Gift of Donald McKay Frost

As early as the Seventies Whistler had shown an interest in typography and layout, and he designed a number of his own pamphlets and catalogues. The simplicity, restraint, and asymmetry of his pages, and the orientalism of the butterfly device influenced the typographic experiments of the Nineties. His biographers, the Pennells, observed: "He designed the title-page; a design contrary to all established rules, but with the charm, the balance, the harmony, the touch of personality he gave to everything, and since copied and prostituted by foolish imitators who had no conception of its purpose."

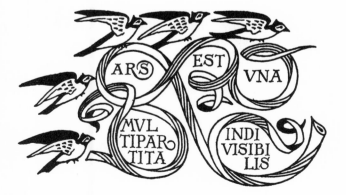

The Gentle Art of Making Enemies is a collection of Whistler's earlier published writings and served as an "artistic autobiography." He called it his Bible. Before this edition was completed, Sheriden Ford's unauthorized edition was printed in Belgium. Four preliminary leaves of Heinemann's edition contain references to this episode, quietly set forth in small, off-center paragraphs with such headings as "An extraordinary piratical plot," "The exploded plot," and "Mr. Whistler's paper hunt."

Ref: Arts Council, *Whistler*, p. 25, 103; Seitz, *Writings by & about Whistler*, p. 3-11, 22; Symons, "An Unacknowledged Movement," p. 89 ill.; Taylor, *The Art Nouveau Book*, p. 50-54; Pennell, *The Life of James McNeill Whistler*, vol. 2, p. 100-113.

4

Michael Field, pseud., *The Tragic Mary*
Selwyn Image, designer of binding
London, George Bell and Sons, 1890

Unillustrated. Printed by the Chiswick Press, Charles Whittingham and Company.

8⁵⁄₁₆ x 6¼ in. Vellum, gilt-stamped on both covers with design of carnations, thistles, pierced heart, crowns and border motto by Selwyn Image, signed with initials *SI*.
No. 1 of 60 large paper copies, with pen and ink bookplate of Maurice Baring by Hilaire Belloc, signed and dated 1897.

Purchased from the Kenneth Matheson Taylor Fund

Selwyn Image, an artist and craftsman who later became Slade Professor of Fine Arts at Oxford, designed covers for the first numbers of the *Hobby Horse* in 1884. This organ of The Century Guild stressed the importance of all the arts, an attitude reflected in Image's own career. In the covers for *The Tragic Mary* he has woven together motifs associated with Mary Stuart, including her motto, "En ma fin est mon commencement." The same cover design was printed in black on brown paper for the regular copies.
Michael Field was the pseudonym of Katharine Bradley and Edith Cooper, aunt and niece who col-

laborated on many books (Nos. 16, 21). While the reviews were hostile, Meredith wrote Michael Field a letter in praise of *The Tragic Mary* (a phrase borrowed from Walter Pater), and a lifelong friendship with Ricketts ensued when he wrote the authors a letter of vivid admiration after reading the book. Oscar Wilde told them that *The Tragic Mary* and Rossetti's *Poems* were the two most beautifully designed books of the century, but that he was going to surpass them with his *A House of Pomegranates* (No. 6).

Ref: White, "The Artistic Decoration of Cloth Book Covers," p. 16, 23 ill.; Symons, "An Unacknowledged Movement," p. 112; Field, *Works and Days*, p. xvii, 70, 117, 118, 139.

5

Geoffrey Chaucer, *The Works of Geoffrey Chaucer, now Newly Imprinted*
F. S. Ellis, editor
Sir Edward Burne-Jones, illustrator; *William Morris,* designer
Hammersmith, London, Kelmscott Press, 1896

87 wood-engravings designed by Burne-Jones and cut by W. H. Hooper; borders, initials, and "Chaucer" type designed by Morris.

First copy: 16½ x 11 in. One of 13 copies on vellum. Edition of 438 copies (13 vellum, 425 paper).

Gift of Henry Arthur Jones

Second copy: 16½ x 11 in. One of 425 copies on laid paper, with original ex-libris drawing by Burne-Jones, signed with his initials and dated *1896*.

Gift of William B. Osgood Field

Both copies bound in white pigskin by Douglas Cockerell in T. J. Cobden-Sanderson's studio at the Doves Bindery, 1898 and 1900 respectively, after a design by Morris (2 vellum and 46 paper copies thus bound).

William Morris founded the Kelmscott Press in 1891, and he published more than forty books before his death in 1896, five months after the completion of the Chaucer, a monument of Victorian book-

building. Morris' medievalism and his mastery of detail are strongly expressed in this large folio, for which he designed the title-page, borders, initials, type, and binding. The same absorption in the Middle Ages, a heritage of the Pre-Raphaelites, is apparent in the flat, linear, and elongated figures by Burne-Jones, his friend and collaborator since their student days at Oxford. It was to Morris, the great reformer of nineteenth-century design, that subsequent book artists in England and the Continent turned.

Ref: Vallance, *William Morris*, p. 406f.; Crow, *William Morris Designer*, p. 94f.; Zapf, *William Morris*; Brown University Library, *William Morris and the Kelmscott Press*, p. 27-31; Henderson, *William Morris*, p. 327f.; Watkinson, *William Morris as Designer*, p. 57f.; McLean, *Modern Book Design*, p. 7-12; Cockerell, *A Short History and Description of the Kelmscott Press*.

6

Oscar Wilde, *A House of Pomegranates*
Charles Ricketts and *Charles Hazlewood Shannon,* illustrators
Dedicated to Constance Mary Wilde
London, James R. Osgood, McIlvaine and Company, 1891

5 woodcuts designed by Shannon and signed with initials of cutter, *WHD*; pictorial title, 12 illustrations, and ornaments designed by Ricketts, some signed with initials *CR*. Printed by the Chiswick Press, Charles Whittingham and Company.

8¼ x 6¾ in. Half moss-green cloth, ivory-white cloth sides, upper cover stamped in gilt and pale coral with peacock and floral design by Ricketts, pale olive end papers with design of quail and sheaves of corn by Ricketts, signed with initials *CR*. One of an edition of 1000 copies.

Bequest of Evert Jansen Wendell

Charles Ricketts and Charles Shannon, both trained as wood-engravers, were associated in 1889 in the publication of *The Dial,* of which five numbers appeared in eight years. Meticulous craftsmen, they usually cut their own blocks, and in 1896 founded their own Vale Press (No. 12), which maintained impeccable standards of printing. The commercial production of *A House of Pomegranates* is technically inferior to their own publications, and the reproduction of Shannon's blocks, printed in France, very faint. More successful are Ricketts' ornamental vignettes, many of which use the motif of the pomegranate. His earliest experiments in book design were for Osgood, McIlvaine, and he later observed that "though not always strictly shaped according to my wishes, they were unlike the ordinary books in the matter of title page, proportion of margin, and in the designs upon their boards." *A House of Pomegranates* was not a success, and the stock was remaindered about 1903 or 1904. Oscar Wilde wrote of *A House of Pomegranates* that "Mr. Shannon is the drawer of the dreams, and Mr. Ricketts is the subtle and fantastic decorator." It was apropos of a criticism of the cover that Wilde wrote his letter to *The Speaker*:

"What the gilt notes suggest, what imitative parallel may be found to them in that chaos that is termed Nature, is a matter of no importance. They may suggest, as they do sometimes to me, peacocks and pomegranates and splashing fountains of gold water, or, as they do to your critic, sponges and Indian clubs and chimney-pot hats. Such suggestions and evocations have nothing whatsoever to do with the aesthetic quality and value of the design. A thing in Nature becomes much lovelier if it reminds us of a thing in Art, but a thing in Art gains no real beauty through reminding us of a thing in Nature. . . ."

Ref: Symons, "An Unacknowledged Movement," p. 102; Schmutzler, *Art Nouveau*, p. 64, 185-186 ill. and fig. 10; Ricketts, *A Defense of the Revival of Printing*, p. 18; Field, *Works and Days*, p. 139; Rothenstein, *Men and Memories*, vol. 1. p. 133, 198; Jullian, *Oscar Wilde*, p. 191-193; Mason, *Bibliography of Oscar Wilde*, p. 362-369; Wilde, *Decorative Arts in America*, p. 124.

7

John Addington Symonds, *In the Key of Blue and other Prose Poems*
Charles Ricketts, designer of binding
London, Elkin Mathews and John Lane; New York, Macmillan and Company, 1893

Unillustrated. Printed by Ballantyne, Hanson and Company.

7¾ x 5½ in. White cloth, gilt-stamped on both covers with design of S-curved fronds of lily of the valley (described in back of book as "hyacinth and laurel") by Charles Ricketts, signed with initials *CR* and *HLS* (Henry Leighton, sc., binder).

Gift of Peter A. Wick

Covers were sometimes gilt-stamped on white cloth to simulate vellum. In his early designs, Ricketts may have been influenced by Selwyn Image's intricate cover for *The Tragic Mary* (No. 4). The naturalistic design for this cover of *In the Key of Blue* seems to be a transition from the somewhat over-complex pattern of *The House of Pomegranates* to the greater clarity and simplicity of his later work. A few copies were bound in light blue cloth. Elkin Mathews was quoted as saying that all copies were to be so bound, but Ricketts objected, making a jest about "Ricketts' blue," so white cloth was substituted. Although Symonds died in 1893, his style of *belles lettres*, as the publisher termed his work, was congenial to the tastes of the Nineties. The book derives its title from the first sketch, a study in tonalities in which the author poses the blue-clad Venetian *facchino* Augusto in various "symphonies and harmonies of blue." Oscar Wilde on his tour of America had quoted Keats' Sonnet on Blue to exemplify the poet's delicate sense of color harmonies. Wilde submitted an essay on the subject to the first issue of *Hobby Horse*, 1886.

Ref: White, "The Artistic Decoration of Cloth Book-Covers," p. 17 ill.; New York, The Museum of Modern Art, *Art Nouveau*, p. 21 ill.; Babington, *Bibliography of J. A. Symonds*, no. 56.

8

John Gray, *Silverpoints*
Charles Ricketts, designer
London, Elkin Mathews and John Lane at the Sign of the Bodley Head, 1893

Unillustrated. Initials designed by Ricketts. Colophon with initials *CR* and 3 leaves. Printed by R. Folkard and Son.

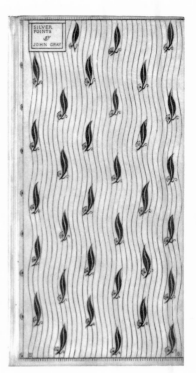

8. Charles Ricketts. Binding for *Silverpoints*. 1893

10. Charles Ricketts. Binding for *The Sphinx*. 1894

7. **Charles Ricketts. Binding for *In the Key of Blue*. 1893**

First copy: 8⅜ x 4 in. Vellum, gilt-stamped on both covers with title in upper left corner and water and willow leaf design by Ricketts, signed with initials *CR* and *HLS* (Henry Leighton, sc., binder).
No. 21 of 25 thick paper copies on paper watermarked Spalding. Edition of 275 copies (25 thick paper, 250 regular, including 50 *hors commerce*).

Gift of Harold Wilmerding Bell

Second copy: 8⅜ x 4 in. Light green cloth, gilt-stamped like first copy. No. 21 of 250 regular copies on paper watermarked Van Gelder.

Gift of Philip Hofer

Silverpoints, simple and novel in slender format, is considered to be Ricketts' most successful trade book, a preliminary to the Vale Press. He based the design on Aldine models and referred to the elongated shape as a "saddle book," attributing it to Persian sources that pentrated Venice. So successful was the cover design that it was copied in various media, and Ricketts noted in 1899 that "the cover of the 'Silverpoints' published in an art paper has drifted back to me from places where my name is quite unknown on bindings, end-papers, wall-papers, and dress cretonnes." The Ricketts monogram and its placement on the final leaf is reminiscent of Whistler's butterfly signature.
John Gray, a fastidious dandy and disciple of the French Symbolists and a member of the Ricketts circle, dedicated one of these poems, "Crocuses in Grass," to Charles Shannon; others were dedicated to Oscar Wilde (who is said to have financed the book), Ernest Dowson, Frank Harris, and Ellen Terry, and to Paul Verlaine, Pierre Louÿs, and Félix Fénéon.

Ref: Ricketts, *A Defense of the Revival of Printing,* p. 20-21; White, "The Artistic Decoration of Cloth Book-Covers," p. 18, 23 ill.; Uzanne, *L'Art dans la Décoration des Livres,* ff. p. 160 ill.; Symons, "An Unacknowledged Movement," p. 103-105 ill.; Rothenstein, *Men and Memories,* vol. 1, p. 175; Taylor, *The Art Nouveau Book,* p. 82 ill.; Jullian, *Oscar Wilde,* p. 166-167.

9

Longus Sophista, *Daphnis and Chloe*
George Thornley, translator

Charles Shannon and *Charles Ricketts,* illustrators
Dedicated to T.S.M. (T. Sturge Moore)
London, Elkin Mathews and John Lane at the Sign of the Bodley Head, 1893

37 woodcuts designed by Shannon and Ricketts, drawn on wood by Ricketts, and engraved by both Shannon and Ricketts. Printed by the Ballantyne Press.

11¼ x 8⅜ in. Green morocco, gilt extra, bound by Rivière for Harold Wilmerding Bell.
One of 200 regular copies. Edition of 210 copies, including 10 *hors commerce*.

Gift of Harold Wilmerding Bell

Ricketts' own description of the *Daphnis and Chloe,* which he considered an early Vale Press book, underlines the obvious Italian Renaissance source and indicates the role each of the partners played: "I was by that time, as I am still, utterly won over and fascinated by the sunny pages of the Venetian printers: I would define the pages of a fine Kelmscott book as full of wine, an Italian book as full of light. In 1892 I was already engaged with my friend Shannon in the carrying out of 'Daphnis and Chloe'; the engraving alone of the pictures and initials occupied us for eleven months. This was terminated in 1893, the book being under press for some time, set up in sections, printed and dispersed piece by piece. I still view this work with great affection, though poorly printed and over-crowded by initials and lines in capitals, that over-set at times the proper balance between the illustrations and the text in a manner not foreseen by us. I hope some day to reprint this wonderful and unknown English text with those amendments in type and design that I have now won by experience in the handling of books. Fifteen of the pictures were sketched by Shannon, revised and drawn on the wood by me: bearing in mind that I engraved each initial, the balance of the engraving in the illustrations rests with Shannon."
Creeping into the generally classical illustrations deriving from the *Hypnerotomachia* are nevertheless some strongly serpentine designs, such as "Love in the Snow" on p. 61. An unexpected note of humor is found in the illustration of the wedding

I MARRIED A WIFE, MY DEAR SONS, when I was yet very young, and, after a while, as I conjectured I should, it was my happinesse to be a Father. For first I had a son born, the second a daughter, and then Astylus the third. I thought there was enow of the

97

9. Charles Shannon and Charles Ricketts. Illustration for *Daphnis and Chloe.* 1893

feast on p. 97, attended by the artists themselves and their friends. As identified by C. J. Holmes, one of the group: "On the extreme right the artists are shown, Ricketts, Shannon, Sturge Moore, Lucien Pissarro, Reginald Savage; the figure standing behind them is Mr. Riley [a friend and associate on *The Dial*], and on the opposite side of the table to the artists (the opposition was deliberate) sits an unfamiliar Holmes. As Ricketts sat at work among us one evening, some remark made him rock with laughter, and I heard him say, 'Oh damn! I've run the graver through Holmes's moustache. It must come out.' And out it came."

Ref: Ricketts, *A Bibliography*, p. xviii; Ricketts, *A Defense of the Revival of Printing*, p. 19-20; Holmes, *Self & Partners*, p. 169; *The Dial*, no. III (1893), ill. after p. 26.

10

Oscar Wilde, *The Sphinx*
Charles Ricketts, designer and illustrator
Dedicated to Marcel Schwob
London, Elkin Mathews and John Lane at the Sign of the Bodley Head; Boston, Copeland and Day, 1894

Pictorial title and 9 illustrations by Ricketts printed in dark red; initials by Ricketts in green. Printed by the Ballantyne Press.

First copy: 10 x 7⅜ in. Large paper copy. Vellum, gilt-stamped on both covers with sphinx design and lower border by Ricketts, signed with initials *CR* and *HL* (Henry Leighton, binder). One of 25 deluxe large paper copies with lower border on binding and with ties. Edition of 225 copies (200 regular, 25 deluxe large paper). Only the large paper copies carry the imprint of Copeland and Day, omitted from the regular copies, but added on a label inserted in the American edition.

Gift of Davenport Brown

Second copy: 8⁹⁄₁₆ x 6¾ in. Vellum, gilt-stamped on both covers with sphinx design by Ricketts without lower border, signed with initials *CR* and *HL*.

Gift of Philip Hofer

Wilde requested Ricketts to design this first edition of *The Sphinx*, and it is the first book over which he exercised complete control of illustration, page, and binding design. His use of a pictorial title, placed on a verso like a frontispiece, was to continue in many of his later publications. Ricketts' own statement gives some insight into the design: "Before I designed my type I built, decorated, and bound 'The Sphinx,' a poem by Oscar Wilde, not strictly a Vale book, since it is without woodcuts; it was published shortly after the 'Hero and Leander,' but was finished before it. "This is the first book of the modern revival printed in three colours, red, black and green: the small bulk of the text and unusual length of the lines necessitated quite a peculiar arrangement of the text; here I made an effort away from the Renaissance towards a book marked by surviving classical traits, printing it in Capitals. In the pictures I have striven to combine, consciously or unconsciously, those affinities in line work broadcast in all epochs. My attempt there as elsewhere was to evolve what one might imagine as possible in one charmed moment or place, just as some great Italian masters painted as they thought in the antique manner, studying like Piero della Francesca, for instance, to fulfil the conditions laid down by Apelles, whom he had of course never seen, but had taken on trust: I advance this example to screen my avowals of indebtedness and research from those perpetual and alternating charges of plagiarism or of eccentricity levelled at all original (i.e., unusual) impulse or effort."

Ref: Ricketts, *A Defense of the Revival of Printing*, p. 24-26; Symons, "An Unacknowledged Movement," p. 106 ill.; Moore, *Charles Ricketts*, introduction, pl. xxx-xxxiii; Taylor, *The Art Nouveau Book*, p. 83 ill.; Holmes, *Self & Partners*; Schmutzler, *Art Nouveau*, p. 86, 185 ill.; *The Dial*, no. III (1893), ill. after p. 18; Mason, *Bibliography of Oscar Wilde*, p. 392-400 ill.; Wilde, *Decorative Art in America*, p. 263-264.

10a

Charles Ricketts, *Melancholia*
Drawing for pictorial title of *The Sphinx*
Pen and ink on paper with a pinkish cast, signed lower left with monogram *CR*.
7⅛ x 5½ in.

10a. Charles Ricketts. *Melancholia*, drawing for *The Sphinx*. 1894

Lent by Mrs. Donald F. Hyde
Formerly colls. Charles Shannon and Lawrence W. Hodgson

The Melancholia drawing for the frontispiece is one of the most sensitive of Ricketts' pen studies. It combines Gothic austerity, a kind of claustral purity, with a touching Beauty and the Beast relationship. The delicate flow and texture of line and rhythmic interlace of the grapevine is the epitome of the decorative quality of Art Nouveau.

Ref.: Moore, *Charles Ricketts*, pl. xxxi.

10b
Charles Ricketts, *The Nereid*
Drawing for *The Sphinx*
Pen and ink on ivory-colored paper.
8¾ x 6½ in. (sight).

Lent by the Fogg Art Museum,
Grenville L. Winthrop Bequest

Ricketts' first treatment of the Oedipus and the Sphinx subject is an Ingresque drawing with overtones of Moreau, executed on commission in 1891 for Sir Frederick Leighton, PRA, for five pounds, and hung by Leighton with two other favorites, a Walter West and an Anning Bell. At the Leighton sale Ricketts repurchased the drawing, and subsequently it passed to Sir William Rothenstein.
The seven Ricketts drawings in the Winthrop collection in the Fogg Museum belong to the second unpublished series of drawings for *The Sphinx*, executed a score of years later. They appear to lack the spontaneous lyric quality of the first series, but the simplified outlines create a broader and grander conception.

Ref: Moore, *Charles Ricketts,* introduction and pl. xxxvi; Ricketts, *Self-Portrait*, p. 19; Holmes, *Self & Partners,* p. 164, 166.

11
Christopher Marlowe, *Hero and Leander*
Charles Ricketts and *Charles Shannon,* illustrators

London, Elkin Mathews and John Lane at the Sign of the Bodley Head, 1894

Pictorial title and 6 illustrations designed and cut on wood by Ricketts and Shannon; border signed with initials *CR*; Vale Press monogram on final leaf. Printed by the Ballantyne Press on paper watermarked with Vale Press monogram.

First copy: 7¾ x 5 in. Vellum, gilt-stamped in geometric design with corner leaves, interlaced initial *C*'s, and date *mdcccxciv* by Ricketts, signed with initials *CR* and *HL* (Henry Leighton, binder). One of 6 copies so bound. One of 200 regular copies. Edition of 220 copies (200 regular, 20 *hors commerce*).

Gift of Paul J. Sachs

Second copy: Vellum blind-stamped in same design.
One of 200 regular copies.

Gift of Philip Hofer

Hero and Leander, like *Daphnis and Chloe* (No. 9) is one of the earliest Vale Press books, published by Elkin Mathews and John Lane and produced by Ricketts and Shannon before Llewellyn Hacon joined them. The press was named for "The Vale," the house Ricketts and Shannon shared in a cul-de-sac on King's Road in Chelsea. The effective small cuts combine the style of the early Florentine woodcut with the elongated Pre-Raphaelite figure style. To obtain unity of effect in this book and also in *Daphnis and Chloe,* Ricketts drew all the designs on the blocks, though half were of Shannon's invention. The schematic floral press mark in the early Vale books bears the initials *SR* (Shannon, Ricketts), later changed to *LHR* (Llewellyn Hacon, Ricketts).
Ricketts comments in his *Defense of the Revival of Printing*: "In 1894 'Hero and Leander' was printed in a smaller size Pica than the 'Daphnis and Chloe': it is the first Vale book with paper bearing as water mark a VP interlaced with a leaf of wild thyme. An interlaced VP with a rose and initials figures in this edition as an imprint, with a motto since discarded, 'The Rose reborn between the leaves,' forgotten, shut away in a book. The small leaf in outline is the first paragraph mark

used in the Vale press. I engraved it on the wood like some used subsequently and it was cast as type. 'The Hero and Leander' is well printed and in margin and proportion of page quite what I would do now. Six copies exist bound as originally intended in blind tooling and gold."

Ref: Ricketts, *A Bibliography,* p. xviii; Moore, *Charles Ricketts,* pl. xxxviii, xxxlx; Ricketts, *A Defense of the Revival of Printing,* p. 22; Ricketts, *Self-Portrait,* footnote p. 69-70; Schmutzler, *Art Nouveau,* p. 185 ill.

12

John Milton, *Early Poems*
Charles Sturt, editor
Charles Ricketts, designer and illustrator
London, Hacon and Ricketts at the Sign of the Dial (Vale Press), 1896

Pictorial title, border, and initials designed and cut on wood by Ricketts; frontispiece signed with initials *CR*; Vale Press monogram on final leaf. Printed by the Ballantyne Press in Vale type on paper watermarked with Vale Press monogram.

10 x 7⁹⁄₁₆ in. White cloth, spine gilt-stamped with title. One of 300 regular copies. Edition of 310 copies (300 regular, 10 *hors commerce*).

Purchased from Duplicate Sale Funds

Milton's *Early Poems* is the first book listed by Ricketts in his bibliography of the books issued by Hacon and Ricketts. W. Llewellyn Hacon was introduced to Ricketts and Shannon by William Rothenstein and became the financial backer of the Press, which issued over forty titles between 1896 and 1904. In that period Ricketts designed three founts cut by W. Prince – the Vale, the Avon and the King's, the last the fount that Ricketts personally favored. Ricketts destroyed them in 1904 by casting the punches and matrices into the Thames and melting the type metal lest they "should drift into other hands than their designers' and become stale by unthinking use." Ricketts was the designer of all the books, and both he and Shannon did illustrations. A small shop was located off Regent Street, for which Shannon painted the "Dial" sign, and C. J. Holmes, later Director of the National Gallery, acted as manager. The partners never owned a press, but Ricketts supervised the printing of all their books at the Ballantyne Press.

Speaking of the frontispiece of this volume, H. C. Marillier says: "It is interesting to compare this with one of the Kelmscott frontispieces in order to realize how completely individual is each case, and how different is the design of the borders. There is nothing in all the flowing tracery of William Morris which remotely resembles the intricate knotwork and geometrical orderliness of the Milton borders." Although Shannon's name does not appear in this book nor the reference to it in Ricketts' bibliography, he recorded in *A Defense of the Revival of Printing* that Shannon helped to cut the frontispiece block.

The Milton book exemplifies Ricketts' principals of typographic layout as based on Morris' statement on the Kelmscott books: that the position of the printed matter on the page should always leave the inner margin the narrowest, the top somewhat wider, the outside (fore-edge) wider still, and the bottom widest of all, based on the medieval rule of a twenty percent difference.

Ricketts continues: "From the essentials of this rule I have never departed in the Vale books. . . . The rough and ready rule of thumb that the difference should be twenty percent between the margins, should be valuable to those once famous printers north of the Tweed, or in any other provincial towns besides Edinburgh, such as Boston, U.S.A. . . ."

Ref: Ricketts, *A Bibliography,* p. iv, xix; Holmes, *Self & Partners,* p. 163-181; Rothenstein, *Men and Memories,* vol. 1, p. 173-176, 199-201; Ricketts, *Self-Portrait,* p. 54-55, 68, 76; Jackson, *The Eighteen Nineties,* p. 263; Ricketts, *A Defense of the Revival of Printing,* p. 22-23.

13

John Gray, *Spiritual Poems, Chiefly Done out of Several Languages*
Charles Ricketts, designer and illustrator
London, Hacon and Ricketts (Vale Press), 1896

Frontispiece and border designed and cut by Ricketts; frontispiece signed with initials *CR* and *JG*.

INRI'

THE TREE
OF
KNOWLEDGE.

ROM what
meek jewel
seed
  Did this
  tree spring?
How first beat its new life
in bleak abode
Of virgin rock, strange met-
als for its food,
Towards its last hewn
mould, the bitter rood?
First did it sprout, indeed,
  A double wing.

13. Charles Ricketts. Frontispiece and border design for *Spiritual Poems*. 1896

Printed at the Ballantyne Press in Vale type on paper watermarked with Vale Press monogram.

7½ x 4¾ in. Brown morocco, gilt-stamped by Rivière.
One of 210 copies.

Gift of Harold Wilmerding Bell

Ricketts' border combines a traditional arrangement with unexpected and even eccentric details, for the two sides are not identical. The symbols of Christ's Passion are arranged in a contained composition at the foot of the page, but at the top, the cross, the lance, and the ladder appear from behind the text and press against the upper margin. The elongated figure of the frontispiece, flattened and simplified, reaches out of her niche to light the lamp against a heavily textured background recalling the grain of the wood block and also the marking of peacock feathers, so popular a decoration at that time. Since John Gray's initials were added to Ricketts', he must have played a role in the formation of this design.

Ref: Ricketts, *A Bibliography,* p. xix-xx.

14

Michael Drayton, *Nymphidia and the Mvses Elizivm*
John Gray, editor
Charles Ricketts, designer and illustrator
London, Hacon and Ricketts at the Sign of the Dial (Vale Press), 1896

Pictorial title and border designed and cut on wood by Ricketts; border signed with initials *CR*. Printed at the Ballantyne Press in Vale type on paper watermarked with Vale Press monogram.

9 x 5½ in. Half white laid paper, printed boards with design of mouse and nut in green and buff by Ricketts.
One of 210 copies.

Gift of W. B. Osgood Field

Ref: Ricketts, *A Bibliography,* p. xx; "Studio Talk," IX 1897, p. 64; Taylor, *The Art Nouveau Book,* p. 88 ill.; Schmutzler, *Art Nouveau,* p. 184-185 ill.

15

The Pageant
Charles Hazelwood Shannon and J. W. Gleeson White, editors
Charles Ricketts, designer
London, Henry and Company, 1896-1897. 2 numbers.

Pictorial title designed by Selwyn Image, signed with initials *SI*.
Reproductions of drawings and paintings by Dante Gabriel Rossetti, James McNeill Whistler, Charles Ricketts, Sir John Everett Millais, William Rothenstein, Charles Conder, Reginald Savage, G. F. Watts, Sir Edward Burne-Jones, Laurence Housman, and Charles H. Shannon in the first number. Printed by T. and A. Constable, by Thomas Way (the Whistler lithographic portrait), and by the Swan Electric Engraving Company.

No. 1: 10 x 7¼ in. Original plum cloth, gilt-stamped on upper cover with bird and branch design by Charles Ricketts, signed with initials *CR*; white end papers with brown frieze design of figures with flowers by Lucien Pissarro. Inscription in ink on flyleaf: *Alice Swinburne from her affectionate brother Algernon Charles Swinburne. Twelfth Day 1896.*

Gift of H. B. Vander Poel

Shannon was the art editor and White the literary editor of *The Pageant,* which was issued in two numbers only, appearing at the time that *The Yellow Book* (No. 33) and *The Savoy* (No. 34) were also being published. Ricketts supervised the layout and designed the first cover, and White included an article on "The Work of Charles Ricketts." The second number, in 1897, retained from the format of the first only Lucien Pissarro's end papers and introduced a different title-page and cover. *The Pageant* included essays and poems by Verlaine, Maeterlinck, Swinburne, Yeats, Housman, etc.

Ref: Rothenstein, *Men and Memories,* vol. 1, p. 226-228.

ACT I

Scene I

Woodstock: masons rais-
ing the Labyrinth
Enter at a distance King Henry,
Sir Topaz, and Mavis
Ist MASON

YONDER
IS
THE
KING.

IInd MASON
He's aged of late.
Ist MASON
Ay, ay! about the face;
his fiery hair
Is dimmed as if by smoke;
his eyes are hollow,
Yet is he stout in body;
well-nigh young.

16. Charles Ricketts.
Page for *Fair Rosamund*. 1897

16

Michael Field, pseud., *Fair Rosamund*
Charles Ricketts, designer
London, Hacon and Ricketts at the Sign of the Dial
(Vale Press), 1897

Rose border designed and cut on wood by Ricketts, signed with initials *CR*. Printed at the Ballantyne Press in Vale type in red and black.

First copy: 9 x 5½ in. Original half gray-blue paper with rose design in brown by Ricketts, printed label on spine, printed boards with bird and arrow design in buff and green by Ricketts. One of 210 copies.

Gift of Philip Hofer

Second copy: 9 x 5½ in. Half gray paper, printed label on spine, printed boards with flame design in chartreuse, orange, and buff. One of 210 copies.

Bequest of Edward Ray Thompson

Ricketts and Shannon published several books by "the Michael Fields," as Miss Bradley and Miss Cooper were called (No. 4). The four were close friends, and Ricketts chose the furniture for the "Paragon," the Michael Field house in Richmond. Ricketts' bibliography notes that the rose border was not used again after this tale of Henry II and his mistress Rosamund Clifford.
The English fondness for flowers seen in Ricketts' floral borders is reflected in a letter he wrote the Michael Fields from Venice: "Carissimo Maestro, We admired Switzerland and passed through windflowers, cowslips, violets, yellow pansies, strawberry flowers, wild crimson azaleas. In Italy there was still some narcissus before we reached the Lago di Chromo [sic], which deserves its name. After that, small congregations of Solomon's seals — these sent their love to you."

Ref: Ricketts, *A Bibliography*, p. xxi; Rothenstein, *Men and Memories*, vol. 1, p. 202-203, vol. 2, p. 112-116; Field, *Works and Days*, p. xviii; Ricketts, *Self-Portrait*, p. 27.

17

Apuleius Madaurensis, *The Excellent Narration of the Marriage of Cvpide and Psyches*

William Adlington, translator; C. J. Holmes, editor
Charles Ricketts, designer and illustrator
London, Hacon and Ricketts at the Sign of the Dial
(Vale Press), 1897

5 medallion illustrations designed and cut on wood by Ricketts; Vale Press monogram on final leaf. Printed at the Ballantyne Press in Vale type in red and black on paper watermarked with Vale Press monogram.

9 x 5½ in. Green morocco gilt-stamped in geometric design by Ricketts, signed with initials *HR* (Hacon and Ricketts).
One of 310 copies, according to Ricketts' bibliography.

Gift of Harold Wilmerding Bell

Ricketts published some of his early experiments for *Cvpide and Psyches* in various periodicals. The first illustrations were not round, but rectangular, as seen on p. 53 of *The Pageant* (No. 15) of 1896. In issue no. 4 of *The Dial* (1896) is an insert of two leaves of *Cvpide and Psyches,* which is the first published page of the Vale type. It was subsequently reset, and the design of the initial adapted for the illustration of p. 41. Perhaps because of the changes, Ricketts' own description in his bibliography does not agree with this copy. He calls for a border and colophon in Latin, neither of which is present in this copy.

Ref: Ricketts, *A Bibliography*, p. xxviii; Hofstätter, *Jugendstil Druckkunst*, p. 68 ill.; Ricketts, *A Defense of the Revival of Printing*, p. 26, 28-29.

18

Dante Gabriel Rossetti, *The Blessed Damozel*
Charles Ricketts, designer
London, Hacon and Ricketts at the Sign of the Dial
(Vale Press), 1898

Initials designed by Ricketts. Printed at the Ballantyne Press in Vale type in red and black.

3¼ x 4¾ in. Red morocco, gilt-stamped in geometric design with spears of wheat by Ricketts, signed with initials *HR* (Hacon and Ricketts). One of 10 copies on vellum. Edition of 220 copies (10 vellum, 210 paper).

Gift of Harold Wilmerding Bell

The regular paper copies were bound in a figured paper with a design of angels by Ricketts. The colophon lists an edition of 220 copies, Ricketts' bibliography, 320 copies. The poetry of *The Blessed Damozel* reveals the influence of Blake, whom Rossetti and many artists of the Nineties admired.

Ref: Ricketts, *A Bibliography*, p. xxv; Schmutzler, *Art Nouveau*, p. 109.

19

Thomas Chatterton, *The Rowley Poems*
Robert Steele, editor
Charles Ricketts, designer
London, Hacon and Ricketts at the Sign of the Dial (Vale Press), 1898. 2 vols.

2 different borders, including the "wild briony," and initials designed and cut on wood by Ricketts. Printed at the Ballantyne Press in Vale type on paper watermarked with Vale Press monogram.

First copy: 9 x 5½ in. Red morocco, gilt-stamped on both covers with geometric design with double spear of wheat and corner acorns by Ricketts, signed with initials *HR* (Hacon and Ricketts). One of 8 copies on vellum. Edition of 218 copies (8 vellum, 210 regular).

Gift of Harold Wilmerding Bell

Second copy: 9 x 5½ in. Half gray paper with printed label on spine, printed boards with flame design in chartreuse, orange, and buff.

Bequest of Edward Ray Thompson

Ricketts' bibliography describes the binding of the regular copies as his bird and rose design.

Ref: Ricketts, *A Bibliography*, p. xxiv.

20

William Shakespeare, *The Tragedy of Hamlet*
T. S. Moore, editor

Charles Ricketts, designer
London, Hacon and Ricketts; New York, John Lane, 1900

Frontispiece, Vale Press device of graver and wreath, border, and half borders designed by Ricketts. Borders, Vale Press device, and the two alphabets on title-page cut on brass by Messrs. Knight and Cottrell; half borders engraved on wood by C. Keats. Printed at the Ballantyne Press in Avon type on paper watermarked with Vale Press mermaid mark.

9⅛ x 5⅝ in. Green cloth, blind-stamped in geometric design with single sheaf of wheat and corner leaves by Ricketts.

Gift of Philip Hofer

Hamlet was the first play of the Vale Shakespeare, issued in thirty-nine volumes from 1900 to 1903. Ricketts designed the Avon type for the set, and also three separate borders for the tragedies, comedies, and histories. The frontispiece design of the burning phoenix in a palm with the motto, "Valeo, non vale dico," was used in the Hamlet as a reference to a recent fire at the Ballantyne Press that had destroyed many of the Vale Press blocks. The device was repeated in the final volume, *King Richard III* with the punning motto altered to "Valeo, sed Vale dico." All the Shakespeare volumes were uniformly bound in green cloth, stamped in Ricketts' design similar to that executed in red morocco for vellum copies of the *Rowley Poems* (No. 19).

Ref: Ricketts, *A Bibliography*, p. xxxi-xxxii; Holmes, *Self & Partners*, p. 173, 175.

21

Michael Field, pseud., *Julia Domna*
Charles Ricketts, designer and illustrator
London, Hacon and Ricketts; New York, John Lane, 1903

Illustration and border designed and cut on wood by Ricketts, signed with initials *CR*. Printed at the Ballantyne Press in Vale type in red and black on paper watermarked with Vale Press monogram.

First copy: 9¼ x 5½ in. Limp vellum, gilt-stamped spine. One of 10 copies on vellum. Edition of 250 copies (10 vellum, 240 regular).

Gift of Harold Wilmerding Bell

Second copy: 9½ x 5½ in. Original half gray paper, printed label on spine, printed boards with peacock design in green on buff by Ricketts.
One of 240 regular copies.

Gift of the class of 1895 in memory of George Cabot Lodge and Trumbull Stickney

The Medusa mask at the foot of the title border suggests an antique cameo infused with the sardonic spirit of Art Nouveau.

Ref: Ricketts, *A Bibliography,* p. xxx.

22

Christina Rossetti, *Goblin Market*
Laurence Housman, illustrator
London, Macmillan and Company, 1893

Pictorial title, 12 illustrations and vignettes, some signed with initials *LH*. Printed by R. and R. Clark, Edinburgh.

First copy: 10¼ x 6⅝ in. Large paper copy. Green cloth, printed label on spine. One of 160 large paper copies.

Bequest of Amy Lowell

Second copy: 6⅛ x 3¾ in. Green morocco, gilt-stamped spine and corners in acorn and leaf design, signed with initials *EGS* and dated *1900*.
Bequest of W. K. Richardson

Laurence Housman (younger brother of A. E. Housman), and his sister Clemence, like Charles Ricketts and Charles Shannon, studied wood-engraving at the City and Guilds Technical Institute in the Kennington Road, London. Laurence did considerable illustration before making his name in literature, and Clemence engraved most of his work. He chose to illustrate *Goblin Market,* with the permission of the publisher and author, but Christina Rossetti was not happy with the results. "I don't think my Goblins were quite so ugly," she commented. Her brother Dante Gabriel had illustrated the first edition of 1862 in a decorative Pre-Raphaelite manner. Housman's compressed compositions and sinuous little vignettes have far greater intensity and menace.

Ref: Housman, *The Unexpected Years,* p. 103; "Studio New Publications," II, 1894, p. 145-146 ill.; Uzanne, *L'Art dans la Décoration des Livres,* p. 251 ill.; Symons, "An Unacknowledged Movement," p. 109; McLean, *Modern Book Illustration,* p. 32, pl. 4b; Lewis, *The Twentieth Century Book,* p. 148 ill.; Taylor, *The Art Nouveau Book,* p. 104f. ill.

23

Jane Barlow, *The End of Elfintown*
Laurence Housman, illustrator
London, Macmillan and Company, 1894

Pictorial title, 8 illustrations and vignettes, some signed with initials *LH*. Printed by R. and R. Clark, Edinburgh.

7 x 4⅝ in. Buff cloth, gilt-stamped on both covers with title and foliated spiral design by Housman, repeated in orange and cream jacket.

Ref: Housman, *The Unexpected Years,* p. 136; "Studio New Publications," IV, 1894, p. xli; Symons, "An Unacknowledged Movement," p. 109-110; Taylor, *The Art Nouveau Book,* p. 104f. ill.; Schmutzler, *Art Nouveau,* p. 186 ill.

Ref: Housman, *The Unexpected Years,* p. 137; "Studio Reviews of Recent Publications," IX, 1897, p. 220 ill.; Bodenhausen, "Das Englische Buch," p. 339 ill.; Uzanne, *L'Art dans la Décoration des Livres,* opp. p. 153 ill.; Symons, "An Unacknowledged Movement," p. 111; Lewis, *The Twentieth Century Book,* p. 24 ill.; Taylor, *The Art Nouveau Book,* p. 104f. ill.

25

Malcolm Bell, *Sir Edward Burne-Jones, a Record and Review*
Gleeson White, designer of binding
London and New York, George Bell & Sons, 1894.
3rd edition

Illustrated with reproductions of Burne-Jones's work. Printed by Charles Whittingham and Company.

$11\frac{5}{16}$ x 8 in. Light gray-blue cloth, upper cover stamped in standard rose tree design in darker blue-gray by White, title gilt-stamped.

Lent by the Fogg Art Museum Library

Gleeson White, who was an editor of *The Studio,* in 1894 published an article on modern cloth bindings in which he singled out for praise several designers, including Selwyn Image, Aubrey Beardsley, and Charles Ricketts. He pointed out the transience of cloth covers, but maintained that they could nevertheless be well designed if the artist kept in mind the fitness of design to subject and the proportion of design, lettering, and surface. The Department of Printing and Graphic Arts possesses several hundred drawings by Gleeson White for book covers and end papers, including two maquettes for this Burne-Jones cover.

Ref: White, "The Artistic Decoration of Cloth Book Covers," p. 19 ill.; Uzanne, *L'Art dans la Décoration des Livres,* p. 144 ill.

26

Sir Thomas Malory, *Le Morte Darthur*
Aubrey Beardsley, illustrator and designer of binding
London, J. M. Dent & Co., 1893-94. 3 volumes.

24

Laurence Housman, *Green Arras*
Laurence Housman, illustrator
Dedicated to Clemence Housman
London, John Lane at the Bodley Head; Chicago, Way and Williams, 1896

Pictorial title and frontispiece with borders, 5 illustrations (including repetition of frontispiece) by Housman, several signed with initials *LH*. Printed by R. Folkard and Son.

First copy: $7\frac{1}{2}$ x 5 in. Green cloth, upper cover gilt-stamped with arabesque design by Housman, buff end papers with floral design by Housman.

Gift of Peter A. Wick

Second copy: $7\frac{1}{2}$ x 5 in. Bound like first copy, floral end papers lacking.

Bequest of Amy Lowell

Housman's book cover designs were highly commended by contemporary reviewers. In describing this one for the first edition of his own poems, he noted years later, "I was just then designing book covers for John Lane, so naturally I did what I thought an extra-good one for myself. It was, in all events, very rich and elaborate." This design may owe its first suggestion to Ricketts' cover for *Silverpoints* (No. 8), particularly in the placement of the lettering panel in the upper left corner, but the intricate, double-looped, gilt pattern is both personal and cleverly ornamental.

GREEN ARRAS
BY
LAURENCE HOUSMAN

LONDON: JOHN LANE
AT THE BODLEY HEAD
CHICAGO: WAY AND
WILLIAMS   1896

24. Laurence Housman. Title-page for *Green Arras*. 1896

2 photogravure frontispieces, 18 line-block illustrations, numerous vignettes, borders and initials by Beardsley; publisher's device on title-page and some initials printed in red. Printed by Turnbull and Spears, Edinburgh.

First copy: 10 x 7¾ in. One of several copies specially bound in vellum, upper cover gilt-stamped with stylized design of swaying clematis by Beardsley; lower cover with publisher's device; spine gilt-stamped in leaf design with title. No. 143 of 300 copies of "superior issue" on Dutch hand-made paper. Edition: 1800 copies (300 "superior issue," 1500 regular). This copy with 19 original drawings for chapter headings, one publisher's device and one foliated letter *S*, bound in, executed in pen, india ink and chinese white.

Lent by John D. Merriam

Second copy: 9⅞ x 7¾ in. No. 2 of "superior edition" as above. Half green morocco, top edges gilt, by Worsfold.

Gift of Philip Hofer

Third copy: 10⅛ x 8¼ in. Uncut. No. 74 of "superior edition" as above, issued in 12 parts in original printed wrappers in gray paper with landscape design printed in black, signed lower left by Beardsley.

Gift of W. B. Osgood Field

The bookseller Frederick Evans recommended Beardsley to the publisher John Dent, resulting in the commission to illustrate *Le Morte Darthur,* an ambitious undertaking intended to rival the Kelmscott Press books. Beardsley executed over 350 drawings to be reproduced in line-block, a photomechanical process of facsimile reproduction which limited the illustrations to broad flat tones of black and white without intricate line or intermediate values. Beardsley's style at this point was already influenced by Burne-Jones, and the Kelmscott page layout was imitated with a pictorial design enclosed by a floral border. Morris regarded the results as a crude parody and contemplated legal action. The *Morte Darthur* illustrations certainly evince a personalized style — tense, Japonesque, the pictures offset in their frames, with broad flat areas of black and white and exotic stylization — considerably removed from the classic balance and medieval naturalism of the Kelmscott books with their three dimensional interlaced borders.

The *Morte Darthur* closed Beardsley's first period, though indeed his style developed with the saga itself, moving towards the brilliant pantomime which so sharply characterizes *Salome.*

Ref: Taylor, *The Art Nouveau Book*, p. 94-96 ill.; Ross, *Aubrey Beardsley*, p. 42; Reade, *Aubrey Beardsley*, p. 16 and nos. 55-163 ill.; Victoria and Albert Museum, *Beardsley cat.*, nos. 164-233; Symons, "An Unacknowledged Movement," p. 98 ill.

26a

Aubrey Beardsley, *How La Beale Isoud Nursed Sir Tristram*
Drawing for *Le Morte Darthur*, vol. II, Frontispiece. 1893-94
India ink. 11 x 8¾ in.

Anonymous loan

Ref: Reade, *Aubrey Beardsley,* no. 100, pl. 100.

26b

Aubrey Beardsley, *How Sir Tristram Drank of the Love Drink*
Drawing for *Le Morte Darthur*, vol. II, opp. p. 334. 1893–94
India ink. 11 x 8 in.

Anonymous Loan

Ref: Reade, *Aubrey Beardsley,* no. 104, pl. 105.

27

Oscar Wilde, *Salome, a Tragedy in one Act*
Lord Alfred Douglas, translator
Aubrey Beardsley, illustrator and designer of binding
Dedicated to Lord Alfred Douglas
London, Elkin Mathews and John Lane; Boston, Copeland and Day, 1894

Border for title-page and list of illustrations, and

HOW SIR TRISTRAM DRANK OF THE LOVE DRINK

26b. Aubrey Beardsley. *How Sir Tristram Drank of the Love Drink*, drawing for *Le Morte Darthur*. 1893-1894

10 full-page illustrations and tailpiece by Beardsley. Plates engraved by Carl Hentschel.

8¼ x 5⅞ in. Blue cloth, upper cover gilt-stamped with asymmetrical diagram of roses and rose petals, lower cover with Beardsley candle device. One of 500 regular copies. Edition of 600 copies (500 regular, 100 deluxe large paper for England bound in green silk).

Gift of Frank W. Garrison

Towards the end of 1893 Beardsley commenced working for the publisher John Lane, who issued his illustrations for Wilde's *Salome* in 1894. In April of the same year Lane published the first issue of *The Yellow Book*. Joseph Pennell's flattering review in the first issue of *The Studio* had introduced Beardsley to the public and turned the tide of earlier ridicule towards fashionable acceptance. It was the year of the "Beardsley Craze."
Wilde had written *Salomé* in French in 1891 expressly for Sarah Bernhardt. The highly wrought Byzantine opulence of this prose-poem immediately attracted her. She was to open in the title role at the Palace Theatre in 1892, but the British censor intervened.
Beardsley's first meeting with Wilde was in 1891, and his illustrations for this edition were commissioned in 1893. Robert Ross remarked that "in the illustrations to *Salome* Beardsley reached the consummation of the new convention he created for himself; they are collectively his masterpiece." He had received fresh impetus from a series of visits to the Greek vase collection in the British Museum, and to Whistler's famous Peacock Room in Prince's Gate. Walter Crane observed that the one fault in the *Salome* drawings lay in the slick texture of the pictures suggestive of other media than pen and ink.
For the French edition of 1893 Wilde conceived a binding "in Tyrian purple and tired silver," but was not pleased with Lane's pedestrian binding for this edition. "The cover of *Salome* is quite dreadful," he wrote to the publisher, "Don't spoil a lovely book. Have simply a folded vellum wrapper with the design in scarlet — much cheaper, and much better. The texture of the present cover is coarse and common; it is quite impossible and spoils the real beauty of the interior. Use up this horrid Irish stuff for stories etc.: don't inflict it on a work of art like *Salome*. It really will do you a great deal of harm. Everyone will say that it is coarse and inappropriate. I loathe it, so does Beardsley."

Ref: Victoria and Albert Museum, *Beardsley cat.*, no. 364; Reade, *Aubrey Beardsley*, no. 273, pl. 271; Ross, *Aubrey Beardsley*, p. 24, 45-46; Jullian, *Oscar Wilde*, p. 255; Mason, *Bibliography of Oscar Wilde*, p. 369-380.

27a
Aubrey Beardsley, Title-page for *Salome*
Drawing. 1894 (altered for publication, since this study was censored)
Pen, india ink and pencil. 8¾ x 6½ in.
Formerly coll: John Lane

Lent by the Fogg Art Museum,
Grenville L. Winthrop Bequest

Ref: Reade, *Aubrey Beardsley*, no. 274, pl. 274.

27b
Aubrey Beardsley, *The Peacock Skirt*
Drawing for *Salome*, opp. p. 2. 1894
India ink. 9⅛ x 6⅝ in. Signed upper right with artist's device.

Lent by the Fogg Art Museum,
Grenville L. Winthrop Bequest

Ref: Reade, *Aubrey Beardsley*, no. 277, pl. 277.

28
Aubrey Beardsley, *Isolde*
Drawing study for a color lithograph printed in red, gray, green and black, which appeared in a supplement to *The Studio*, October 1895.
Pen, ink and watercolor. 11 x 7⅛ in. Title lower right in pen.

Lent by the Fogg Art Museum,
Grenville L. Winthrop Bequest

Beardsley enjoyed picturing one of his favorite Wagnerian heroines as a fashionably dressed woman of his own period. Placing her in profile gave him the opportunity to silhouette the figure; the upper half, which includes the quite fabulous hat he invented and the chalice, is set against the hectic scarlet of the background.

Ref: Reade, *Aubrey Beardsley,* no. 392, pl. 391.

29

Alexander Pope, *The Rape of the Lock*
Aubrey Beardsley, illustrator and designer of binding
Dedicated to Edmond Gosse
London, Leonard Smithers, 1896

Reproductions of 9 drawings by Beardsley. Printed by the Chiswick Press, Charles Whittingham and Company, with title-page in red and black.

$10\frac{1}{8}$ x $7\frac{1}{2}$ in. Turquoise blue cloth, upper cover gilt-stamped with design by Beardsley of candelabra and mirror framing an open pair of scissors and the lock. Signed at lower left and right corners with initials *A* and *B*. One of regular edition of 500 copies for the so-called "Edition De Luxe." The edition included 25 copies on Japanese vellum.

Gift of Peter A. Wick

Edmond Gosse, who had suggested to Beardsley that he illustrate Pope's "heroi-comical" poem, wrote a letter to the artist, May 16th, 1896 complimenting the book and expressing his belief that never was a subject more suited to Beardsley's genius than *The Rape of the Lock*. The nine "embroidered" drawings, so described on the title-page, are the epitome of Beardsley's brittle, tenuous neo-rococo style. They have the flavor of the satirical drawings of Gian Domenico Tiepolo but lack the eighteenth-century Italian artist's substance and betray their author's hybrid and exotic proliferation. A small "bijou" edition of 1897 had a different cover and repeated some of the plates of the first edition.

Ref: Reade, *Beardsley,* p. 13 and nos. 403-413, pls. 404-411; Victoria and Albert Museum, *Beardsley cat.,* nos. 488, 505, 513.

29a

Aubrey Beardsley, *The Cave of Spleen*
Drawing for *The Rape of the Lock,* opp. p. 24. 1896
India ink. $9\frac{7}{8}$ x $6\frac{7}{8}$ in.

Lent by the Museum of Fine Arts, Boston,
Gift of the Estate of William Sturgis Bigelow

Ref: Reade, *Aubrey Beardsley,* no. 410, pl. 411.

30

Ernest Dowson, *Verses*
Aubrey Beardsley, designer of binding
London, Leonard Smithers, 1896

Unillustrated. Printed by the Chiswick Press, Charles Whittingham and Company.

$7\frac{1}{2}$ x $5\frac{1}{2}$ in. Imitation vellum boards, gilt-stamped in tendril design by Beardsley, signed lower right corner with initials *AB*. One of 300 small paper copies on handmade paper. Edition of 330 copies (300 small paper, 30 large paper on Japanese vellum).

Bequest of Amy Lowell

"The curves of this exceptionally economic design, which is near to nothing, may be said to reflect, in Beardsley's idiosyncratic style, a current art nouveau form."

Ref: Reade, *Aubrey Beardsley,* nos. 260, 457, pl. 457.

31

Ben Johnson, *Volpone: or the Foxe, a new edition*
Aubrey Beardsley, illustrator and designer of binding
New York, John Lane, 1898

Frontispiece, signed with initials *AB*, title-page vignette, and 5 pictorial initials by Beardsley, reproduced from drawings.

11 x $8\frac{1}{2}$ in. Vellum, upper cover gilt-stamped with title and foliate design by Beardsley, signed with

initials *AB, Paris* and dated *1898*, lower left. Book-plate of John Quinn.

No. 43 of 100 copies on Japanese vellum with extra set of plates in large size printed in photogravure. Edition of 1100 copies "for England and America" (100 Japanese vellum, 1000 regular). Leonard Smither's imprint appeared on the copies for England, John Lane's on the copies for America. The regular copies were bound in blue cloth, gilt-stamped with the same design as that on the vellum binding.

Lent by John D. Merriam

The style of the illustrations suggests seventeenth-century engraving. The initials, formed of architectural details, herms, birds and animals, continue the influence of Mantegna, merged with a more robust baroque manner. This edition, which contains a eulogy of Beardsley by Robert Ross, is dedicated to the artist's mother. He was working on the Volpone drawings, of which twenty-four were planned, at the time of his death.

Ref: Reade, *Aubrey Beardsley,* p. 18, 19, nos. and pls. 495-502; Victoria and Albert Museum, *Beardsley cat.,* nos. 581-584; Taylor, *The Art Nouveau Book,* p. 102 ill.

32

Aubrey Beardsley, *Under the Hill and Other Essays in Prose and Verse*
Aubrey Beardsley, illustrator
London and New York, John Lane, the Bodley Head, 1904

Frontispiece photograph of Beardsley, 14 illustrations by Beardsley reproduced from drawings, 2 tailpieces. Printed by Ballantyne, Hanson & Co.

10$\frac{1}{16}$ x 7$\frac{1}{2}$ in. Dark blue cloth, gilt-stamped with design of peacock feathers, signed in the design with Beardsley's device of three candles, upper edges gilt.

Bequest of Amy Lowell

The original cover design was intended for *Salome* (No. 27), but was not used. John Lane had first published four chapters of Beardsley's unfinished novel *Under the Hill,* the final version of his *The Story of Venus and Tannhauser,* with five illustrations by Beardsley and a self-portrait, in the first two issues of *The Savoy* (No. 34).

Ref: Reade, *Beardsley,* no. and pl. 270, 272, 423-5, 428-9; Victoria and Albert Museum, *Beardsley cat.,* no. 447, 528, 529.

33

The Yellow Book, an Illustrated Quarterly
Henry Harland, editor
Aubrey Beardsley, art editor
London, Elkin Mathews and John Lane; Boston, Copeland and Day, 1894-1897. 13 volumes.

Cover designs of first 5 vols. by Beardsley. Reproductions of drawings and paintings by Beardsley, Sir Frederic Leighton, Joseph Pennell, Walter Sickert, William Rothenstein, Laurence Housman, J. T. Nettleship, Charles W. Furse, and R. Anning Bell in 1st vol. Printed by the Ballantyne Press; reproductions by the Swan Electric Engraving Company.

8 x 6$\frac{1}{4}$ in. Yellow cloth, upper cover stamped in black with title and pictorial design, lower covers with contents and borders (by Beardsley in first 5 vols.).

Gift of W. B. Osgood Field

Elkin Mathews and John Lane became partners in 1887 and opened their book shop in Vigo Street, London, under a sign with the head of Sir Thomas Bodley. In 1894 they parted, after the publication of the first two numbers of *The Yellow Book,* a venture sponsored by Lane for which Mathews had little sympathy. Thirteen issues, or volumes, of the quarterly were published in the three years between April, 1894 and April, 1897. The American Henry Harland was the editor and Aubrey Beardsley the art editor. He was dismissed at the time of the Wilde trial by Lane, bowing to unjustified pressures, since Wilde had never contributed to *The Yellow Book* nor been particularly close to Beardsley, who had come to epitomize the decadent taste of the Nineties and was thus victimized. Vol. 4 (January, 1895) is the last issue of *The Yellow Book* in which Beardsley's name appears among the contributors. The covers of vol. 5 (April, 1895) are his design, and the border of the lower cover, repeated from the earlier volumes, is identified by his device of three candles, but his name is omitted. The novelty of *The Yellow Book,* whose early numbers before the departure of Beardsley were the essence of "the new" in art and literature, found a ready public. The bright yellow hard covers, Beardsley's arresting style, and the varied contents combined to produce an immediate success as well as a *succès de scandale.* Over six thousand of the seven thousand copies of the first volume were sold, and of the second volume, four thousand were sold the first month.

The second volume of *The Yellow Book* (July, 1895) includes an unusual feature, a critique of the first by Philip Hamerton (p. 179-190) who observes that in requesting this contribution the editor and publisher seemed to know the value of originality in all things. Hamerton felt that "On the whole, the literature . . . is adequately representative of the modern English literary mind, both in the observation of reality and in style." As for the cover, he felt that "The yellow colour adopted is glaring, and from the aesthetic point of view not so good as a quiet mixed tint might have been. . . ." Overcoming personal taste, he observed that "There is distinctly a sort of corruption in Mr. Beardsley's art so far as its human element is concerned, but not at all in its artistic qualities, which show the perfection of discipline, of self-control, and of thoughtful deliberation at the very moment of invention." Oscar Wilde was less respectful when he said to Charles Ricketts, "My dear Boy, do not say nice false things about the 'Yellow Book.' I bought it at the station, but before I had cut all the pages, I threw it out of my carriage window."

Ref: Jackson, *The Eighteen Nineties,* p. 45-48; Muir, *Minding my own Business,* p. 7-10; Victoria and Albert Museum, *Beardsley cat.,* nos. 393-426, 484-485; Reade, *Beardsley Picture Book,* p. 8-9, pl. 20, 21, 23-28 ill.; Reade, *Beardsley,* p. 17, pl. 352-371.

34

The Savoy, an Illustrated Monthly
Arthur Symons, editor

Aubrey Beardsley, art editor
London, Leonard Smithers, 1896. 8 numbers.

Cover and title-page designs by Aubrey Beardsley. Reproductions of drawings and paintings by Beardsley, Charles Shannon, Charles Conder, Joseph Pennell, Louis Oury, William Rothenstein, F. Sandys, Max Beerbohm and Jacques L. Blanche in 1st vol. Printed by H. S. Nichols (vol. 1 and 2); Chiswick Press, Charles Whittingham and Company (vols. 3-8); wood-engravings, line and half-tone blocks by Paul Nauman.

10¼ x 7¾ in.
Nos. 1-2: pink boards, upper covers stamped in black with title and pictorial design by Beardsley, lower covers with Smithers' device.
Nos. 3-7: light green-blue wrappers, upper covers stamped with title in red, pictorial design by Beardsley in black, lower covers with Pan and Pegasus device.
No. 8: light green-blue wrappers, upper cover stamped in black with title (variant of title in earlier nos.) and pictorial design by Beardsley, lower cover with Pan and Pegasus device.

Gift of W. B. Osgood Field

In the autumn of 1895 Leonard Smithers asked Arthur Symons to form and edit *The Savoy,* and he immediately sought the cooperation of Beardsley, recently discharged from *The Yellow Book* (No. 33), whom he looked upon as "the most individual and expressive draughtsman of our time." The magazine began as a quarterly, but after two numbers became a monthly. Eight numbers were issued from January to December, 1896. Beardsley designed all the covers and many of the illustrations, and two installments of his novel "Under the Hill," with his own illustrations, were included. In the third number it was announced that his illness forced cancellation of succeeding chapters.

Each cover of *The Savoy* is different. The first two numbers have the same title-page, while nos. 3-8 contain a new title-page, a figure of Pan mounted on Pegasus, which also appears as a vignette on the lower covers. It was not a financial success and was forced to discontinue at the end of the year. The final number, with a different cover format, was wholly written by Symons and illustrated by Beardsley. The quality of the magazine was very high. Avoiding the notoriety of *The Yellow Book, The Savoy* is perhaps the most mature and consistent periodical to express the literary and artistic culture of the Nineties in England. In the first number, Symons stated that "All we ask from our contributors is good work, and good work is all we offer our readers. . . . We have no formulas. . . . We have not invented a new point of view." In an epilogue in the final number he observed, "We assumed that there were very many people in the world who really cared for art, and really for art's sake. The more I consider it, the more I realize that this is not the case. Comparatively few people care for art at all, and most of these care for it because they mistake it for something else."

Ref: Jackson, *The Eighteen Nineties,* p. 48-50; Victoria and Albert Museum, *Beardsley cat.,* no. 519-549; Reade, *Beardsley,* no. 414-454 ill.; Reade, *Beardsley Picture Book,* no. 33-35 ill.; Rothenstein, *Men and Memories,* vol. 1, p. 245f.

34a

Poster for *The Savoy*

Aubrey Beardsley, designer

Small poster or show card, lithograph in three colors, vermilion, emerald green and black, with design of Beardsley's front wrapper for *The Savoy,* no. 8, December, 1896. Signed with initials *AB* lower left in design. Printed by C. F. Kell, London.

$9\frac{5}{16}$ x $6\frac{7}{8}$ in.

Gift of Peter A. Wick

The poster advertises the set of the bound volumes in violet cloth containing all eight numbers of *The Savoy.*

Ref: Reade, *Beardsley,* no. and pl. 453; Victoria and Albert Museum, *Beardsley cat.,* nos. 536, 537, 548.

35

Jane Barlow, *The Battle of the Frogs and Mice*

Francis D. Bedford, illustrator

London, Methuen and Company, 1894

Pictorial half-title, decorated title-page, frontispiece, 1 full-page illustration, 5 different borders, and vignettes by Bedford.

$8\frac{1}{2}$ x $6\frac{3}{4}$ in. Green cloth, upper cover and spine stamped with title in red and design of frogs and mice in dark green by Bedford.

Gift of Peter A. Wick

This version of Homer's *Bactrachomyomachia* is not set in type, but reproduced from a hand-lettered text not designed for quick reading. Bedford's witty little woodcut borders of frogs or mice, with plants and flowers surrounding three sides of each text page, combine classical and medieval motifs in an eclecticism typical of the Nineties. An undated American edition was published by Frederick A. Stokes with the same illustrations and cover.

Ref: Vollmer, vol. 1, p. 152; Hofstätter, *Jugendstil Druckkunst,* p. 72 ill.

36

Richard Doddridge Blackmore, *Fringilla, Some Tales in Verse*

Louis Fairfax-Muckley, James Linton, illustrators

London, Elkin Mathews, 1895

Pictorial title-page, 8 illustrations, borders, vignettes and initials by Fairfax-Muckley, signed with initials *LFM,* cut on wood by C. Hentschel; 3 reproductions of illustrations by James Linton. Printed by R. Ffolkard [sic] and Son.

8 x 6 in. Gray-green cloth, stamped on upper cover in dark green with lettering and pictorial design by Fairfax-Muckley, signed with initials *LFM;* lower cover with roundel with bird. Bookplate of Laurence Bernard Gomme and letter from Blackmore to Gomme tipped in.

Purchased from the Amy Lowell Fund

Fairfax-Muckley's illustrations and decorations, rooted as they are in the Pre-Raphaelite and

Pictorial title, frontispiece, and 38 illustrations by Rackham, reproduced from drawings; some signed *A. Rackham* or with initials *AR*. Printed by Turnbull and Spears, Edinburgh, with title-page in red and black.

7½ x 5⅜ in. Dark green cloth, upper cover gilt-stamped with title and design of figures by Rackham, top edges gilt.

Gift of W. B. Osgood Field

When Arthur Rackham was a student, he came under the influence of Charles Ricketts, but developed a more elaborate and colorful style. *The Zankiwank & the Bletherwitch* is one of his earliest illustrated books. Most apparent here is Rackham's interest in the grotesque and caricature, traits always present in his work, but later often subservient to a more lyrical strain. Opposed to the nervous silhouette of the ostrich-like "zankiwank" on the title-page is the girl with the abundant hair, the most conspicuous feminine attribute of the style of the Nineties, later elaborated by Rackham into such figures as his *Undine*. An American edition of *The Zankiwank*, with the same illustrations and binding, was also published in 1896 by Dutton in New York. Six Rackham drawings for the book are in the Berol collection of the Columbia University Libraries.

Ref: Latimore and Haskell, *Rackham Bibliography*, p. 8; Hudson, *Rackham*, p. 166; Baughman, *The Centenary of Rackham*, p. 21.

Burne-Jones tradition, yet carry this eclectic linear style further in the serpentine lines of growth in foliage and hair. This exotic quality of "modern art" was troubling to Blackmore, who had first published *Lorna Doone* in 1869, and he noted in the preface to this 1895 edition of *Fringilla*: "Standing afar, I gaze with doubt at other trimmings which are not mine. They have conquered the taste of the day perhaps, and high art announces them as her last transfiguration."
In the same year there was an American edition of *Fringilla*, illustrated by Will Bradley (No. 134).

Ref: Uzanne, *L'Art dans la Décoration des Livres,* opp. p. 140 ill.; Taylor, *The Art Nouveau Book,* p. 61 ill.; Hofstätter, *Jugendstil Druckkunst,* p. 71 ill.

37
S. J. Adair FitzGerald, *The Zankiwank & the Bletherwitch*
Arthur Rackham, illustrator
London, J. M. Dent and Company, 1896

38
The Book of Job
Introduction by Joseph Jacobs
Herbert Granville Fell, illustrator
London, J. M. Dent and Company; New York, Dodd, Mead and Company, 1896

Decorated title with borders, frontispiece, 23 full-page illustrations, including 3 double-page, borders, half-borders, and vignettes by Fell; some signed with initials *HGF* and with initials of cutter, *IUH*. Printed by Turnbull and Spears, Edinburgh, with title-page in red and black.

9¼ x 7¼ in. Buff cloth, upper cover gilt-stamped with title in foliate panel within foliated border design by Fell.

Lent by John D. Merriam

Herbert Granville Fell's *The Book of Job* is a companion to MacDougall's *The Book of Ruth* (No. 39), both published by Dent and Dodd, Mead in 1896. The two books are the same size, bound

in the same gilt-stamped cloth, set in the same type, with similar layout and use of borders. Although MacDougall's borders are more striking, Fell's illustrations are more powerful, reflecting the influence of Blake's *Book of Job*.

Ref: Thieme-Becker, vol. II, p. 372.

39
The Book of Ruth
Introduction by Ernest Rhys
William Brown MacDougall, illustrator
London, J. M. Dent and Company; New York, Dodd, Mead and Company, 1896

Title-page with vignette and border; 8 illustrations, including 1 double-page, 7 ornamental inscriptions, vignettes, initials, and 16 different borders designed by MacDougall; some signed *W. B. MacDougall* and dated *1896*; some borders signed with initials of cutter *CHS*.
Printed by Turnbull and Spears, Edinburgh, with title-page in red and black.

9¼ x 7¼ in. Buff cloth, upper cover gilt-stamped in floral design by MacDougall.

Purchased from the Caroline Miller Parker Fund

William Brown MacDougall was one of the contributors to *The Evergreen,* the publication of Patrick Geddes, leader of the Edinburgh Arts and Crafts movement. He also contributed to no. 6 of *The Savoy* (No. 34) a delicate drawing somewhat in the Beardsley manner and quite different in character from his book illustration. MacDougall's borders and initials, both more forceful than his illustrations, derive their effect from broad contrasts of black and white. In *The Book of Ruth,* the text is on recto pages only, facing blank versos, each recto page framed with a border and opening with a decorated initial. The separate illustrations, also framed with borders are on recto pages facing ornamental inscriptions with the same borders. This volume is a companion to *The Book of Job,* illustrated by Herbert Granville Fell (No. 38).

Ref: Taylor, *The Art Nouveau Book,* p. 115-116; Hoffstätter, *Jugendstil Druckkunst,* p. 87 (MacDougall ill. incorrectly given to Fred Hyland).

40
John Keats, *Isabella or the Pot of Basil*
William Brown MacDougall, illustrator
London, Kegan Paul, Trench, Trübner and Company, 1898

Half-title, 8 illustrations, 8 ornamental inscriptions, and 16 different borders designed by MacDougall. Printed by Turnbull and Spears, Edinburgh.

First copy: 10⅞ x 7¾ in. Brown cloth, upper cover gilt-stamped in arabesque foliate design by MacDougall, top edges gilt.

Gift of Peter A. Wick

Second copy: 10⅞ x 7¾ in. Green cloth, upper cover blind-stamped in same arabesque foliate design as first copy, top edges gilt.

Gift of John Gregory

Isabella, like *The Book of Ruth* (No. 39), gives prominence to MacDougall's name on the title-

39. William Brown MacDougall. Title-page and illustration for *The Book of Ruth*. 1896

page. The two books are similar in design, with the bordered illustrations on recto pages facing ornamental inscriptions with the same borders. The half-title (reproduced on Cover) is perhaps MacDougall's most original design, an interlacing of elliptical curves with a suggestion of foliage, not based on historical models. The graphic style of this young Scot is virile and fresh, with a curious linear shorthand of flat embroidered textures in the illustrations combined with strong black and white borders. The Beardsley mannerism is apparent but without his effeteness, refinement or wit.

41

Harold Nelson, *Fanny Nelson's Bookplate*

Drawing, pen and ink and gold paint, signed *HN* in composition.

8¾ x 3 in. (comp.)

Lent by Peter A. Wick

This bookplate appeared as frontispiece in *Harold Nelson, His Book of Bookplates,* Edinburgh, 1904. Harold Nelson (1871-1946) was an illustrator of books, including Friedrich de La Motte Fouqué, *Undine and Aslaugh's Knight* (1901) and Carmen Sylva (pseud. for Elizabeth, Queen of Rumania), *A Real Queen's Fairy Book* (1901). Selwyn Image wrote of these bookplates: They "are touched with a lighter spirit. In them there is nothing mystical, nothing 'other-worldly.' They are bright and spirited, while in beauty of drawing it would be hard to find their equals among modern bookplates...."

Ref: "Studio Talk," xix, no. 86 (1900), p. 268-70 ill.

42

William Shakespeare, *The Tempest*
Robert Anning Bell, illustrator
London, Freemantle and Company, 1901

Decorated title-page, frontispiece, 28 full-page and 45 half-page illustrations, vignettes, and initials by Bell, some signed *R. An. Bell* and *R. A. Bell* with initials of cutter, *HFD*. Printed by T. and A. Constable, Edinburgh, with running heads in red.

9½ x 6¾ in. White cloth, upper cover gilt-stamped with title, design of ship in tempest and coat of arms in Renaissance frame, with figures of Caliban and Ariel at sides by Bell; top edges gilt, white end papers (lower cover only) with green design of ships, dolphins and birds by Bell.

Robert Anning Bell, a contributor to *The Yellow Book* (No. 33) and later head of the Department of Design at the Royal College of Art, shared Ricketts' taste for early Italian woodcut illustration. This influence is most apparent in the architectural framework of his pages. Against this background Bell places figures based on earlier prototypes, but elongated, exaggerated, and subtly deformed with a wry and perverse humor.

Ref: Jackson, *The Eighteen Nineties,* p. 283; Lewis, *The Twentieth Century Book,* p. 150, 152 ill.; Taylor, *The Art Nouveau Book,* p. 143.

43

Pierre de Ronsard, *Choix de Sonnets*
Lucien Pissarro, designer and illustrator
London, The Eragny Press for Hacon and Ricketts, 1902

Pictorial title designed and cut on wood by Pissarro; border and initials designed by Lucien Pissarro (border signed with initials *LP*) and cut on wood by Esther Pissarro; Eragny Press device on final leaf. Printed by Esther and Lucien Pissarro at the Eragny Press in red and black on paper watermarked with their monogram *ELP* with two leaves.

8⅜ x 5¾ in. Half gray paper, title gilt-stamped, printed dark gray boards with may blossom design in light gray and green by Lucien Pissarro, signed with initials *LP*.
One of 200 regular copies. Edition of 226 copies, including 26 *hors commerce*.

Gift of Philip Hofer

Because Lucien Pissarro wished to publish illustrated children's books, he learned wood-engraving from Auguste Lepère, to whom he was introduced by his father, the Impressionist painter

Camille Pissarro. In 1890 Lucien settled in London and became a friend of Ricketts and Shannon and a contributor to *The Dial*. In 1898 he and Ricketts published a small book, *De la Typographie et de l'Harmonie de la Page Imprimée,* for which Pissarro designed the paragraph mark cut by Ricketts. The pamphlet was to have been printed by Pissarro, but owing to ill health he set only the first eight pages.

Lucien and his wife Esther (Bensusan) founded the Eragny Press, named for the Pissarro home in Normandy, in 1894, and between that date and 1914 published thirty-two books. Until the closing of the Vale Press, they made use of the Vale type by special arrangement with Ricketts, and their books were issued by Hacon and Ricketts. Lucien then designed his own Brook type, named after the Pissarro studio and house in Hammersmith, and cut by W. Prince, who also cut Ricketts' three founts. Following Ricketts' dramatic gesture, Esther cast the punches into the English channel after World War II, carrying out the request of Lucien, who died in 1944. The type itself is now in the collection of private press types of the Cambridge University Press. Pissarro's designs are more vigorous, the blocks more broadly cut, and his figures more monumental than Ricketts', whose eclecticism was deplored by Camille Pissarro. Many of the Eragny Press books tend to the continental tradition of polychrome, not only red and black, but often sage-green, blue and even gold.

Ref: Pissarro, *Notes on the Eragny Press;* Robb, "The Wood-engravings of Lucien Pissarro"; Balston, *The Cambridge University Collection,* p. v, 29-30; Ricketts, *A Bibliography,* p. 23; Taylor, *The Art Nouveau Book,* p. 121-122 ill.

44

Laurence Binyon, *Dream-Come-True*
Laurence Binyon, illustrator; *Lucien Pissarro,* designer
London, The Eragny Press; New York, John Lane, 1905

Frontispiece designed and cut on wood by Binyon; decorations designed by Lucien Pissarro and cut on wood by Esther Pissarro; border signed with initials *LP*; Pissarro monogram *ELP* with two leaves on leaf a2; Eragny Press device on final leaf. Printed by Esther and Lucien Pissarro at the Eragny Press in Brook type in green, red, and black on paper watermarked with their monogram *ELP* with two leaves.

First copy: 7 x 4 in. Half gray paper, printed label, figured cream boards with green and pink floral design by Lucien Pissarro, signed with initials *LP*. One of 150 regular copies. Edition of 185 copies: 175 paper, including 25 *hors commerce*; 10 vellum, including 2 *hors commerce*.

From the library of Mr. and Mrs. Thomas W. Lamont, presented by their Children

Second copy: 7 x 4 in. Covers like first copy, with bookplate of John Quinn.

Purchased from the William Richards Castle Fund

Literary and artistic circles of London in the Nineties were closely associated. The far-ranging interests and versatility of many English writers of this period are exemplified by Laurence Binyon, poet, Orientalist, and later Keeper of Prints and Drawings in the British Museum. He not only drew, but also cut on wood the illustration for his own book, under the supervision of his friends the Pissarros.

Ref: Pissarro, *Notes on the Eragny Press;* Robb, "The Wood-engravings of Lucien Pissarro"; Balston, *The Cambridge University Collection,* p. v, 29-30; Ricketts, *A Bibliography,* p. 23; Taylor, *The Art Nouveau Book,* p. 121-122 ill.

♣ DREAM·COME·TRUE.

♣ I.

WITHIN THE EYES OF DREAM·COME·TRUE SHINE THE OLD DREAMS OF MY YOUTH. ERE THEY FADED, ERE THEY GREW

DISTANT, THEY WERE BORN ANEW IN HER TRUTH.

WITHIN THE HEART OF DREAM·COME·TRUE LIES MY LIFE, A FOLDED BUD: ALL THAT IS TO HOPE AND DO, JOY AND TRIUMPH, TOIL & RUE, SKIES OF THUNDER, SKIES OF BLUE PULSE IN PULSES OF HER BLOOD. O MAY THE FOUNTAIN LEAP IN FLOOD THE YOUNG SHOOT BRANCH IN LEAFY WOOD, BLEST IN PROMISE THROUGH AND THROUGH BY THE DEAR THOUGHTS OF DREAM·COME·TRUE!

44. Laurence Binyon and Lucien Pissarro. Double-page for *Dream-Come-True*. 1905

45

William Morris, *The Defense of Guenevere and Other Poems*
Jessie M. King, illustrator
Dedicated to Dante Gabriel Rossetti
London and New York, John Lane, The Bodley Head, 1904

Half-title, pictorial title, frontispiece, 29 illustrations including pictorial half-titles, and vignettes by Jessie M. King, reproduced from drawings; several signed with initials *JMK.*

7¾ x 5 in. Red cloth, upper cover gilt-stamped with title and design of decorative figure by Jessie M. King, lower cover gilt-stamped with candle and bird design, top edges gilt.

Gift of Peter A. Wick

Jessie King's work exemplifies the Glasgow style of Art Nouveau, which achieved an international reputation and was regarded with high esteem on the Continent, especially in Austria. The architect Charles Rennie Mackintosh was the leader of "The Four" or "The Four Macs," the group consisting of himself and his wife Margaret Macdonald, her sister Frances Macdonald and the latter's husband, the architect J. Herbert MacNair. Like "The Four," Jessie King was a product of the Glasgow School of Art, and with them she exhibited at the 1902 Turin International Exhibition of Modern Decorative Art, where she won a gold medal for her drawings and watercolors. Her vertical compositions, ornamental use of the rose motif, simple grace, and refinement of detail are characteristic of the Glasgow School. Like Beardsley in his late work, she makes use of dotted and stippled textures, but in a more selective, restrained, wholly individual and feminine manner.

Ref: New York, The Museum of Modern Art, *Art Nouveau,* p. 173; Taylor, *The Art Nouveau Book,* p. 130-138 ill.; Howarth, *Mackintosh,* p. 40, 164-167.

46

John Milton, *Comus, A Masque*
Jessie M. King, illustrator

·OF·MARGARET·SITTING·GLORIOUS·THERE·

45. Jessie M. King. Illustration for *The Defense of Guenevere.* 1904

London, George Routledge and Sons; New York, E. P. Dutton and Company, 1906

Frontispiece, extra pictorial title, 8 illustrations, and tailpiece by Jessie M. King, reproduced by photogravure; several signed *Jessie M. King.* Printed by Richard Clay and Sons.

8¼ x 5½ in. Red-brown cloth, green curved border, upper cover gilt-stamped with title and design of pastoral figure by Jessie M. King.

Lent by John D. Merriam

Comus, like *The Defense of Guenevere* (No. 45) is an example of both the Glasgow School and of Jessie King's highly personal and poetic style. She continued with book illustration into the nineteen thirties, when her manner became broader, and she also experimented with batik design.

Ref: Taylor, *The Art Nouveau Book,* p. 135 ill.

47

Margaret Macdonald, *Bookplate for John Edwards* Drawing, pencil, signed lower left *Margt. Macdonald invt. et delt.* ca. 1896

8⅞ x 6¾ in. (sheet)

Lent by Dr. Thomas Howarth

Margaret Macdonald, member of the Glasgow School's "Four," wife of Charles Rennie Mackintosh, with her sister Frances provided many of the motifs for the group's architectural and decorative designs. They evolved a highly unorthodox style of organic vertically swelling and flowing line in which plant and human form seemed to germinate from a common seed, invariably with a solemn disquieting air of melancholy. In this bookplate the personification of Wisdom shielding her children in the protective cocoon of her hair has a spiritual symbolism viewed through a cruciform structure suggestive of the artist's metalwork design. The Four enjoyed enthusiastic recognition by the Vienna Secession group with whom they first exhibited in 1900. A printed label shows that this bookplate was exhibited at the International Exhibition of Decorative Art in Turin in 1902, where the Scottish section was laid out by Mack-

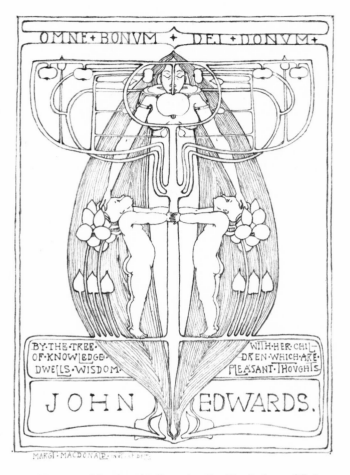

47. Margaret Macdonald. Drawing for Bookplate of John Edwards. ca. 1896

intosh. It was later shown in the Mackintosh Memorial Exhibition in Glasgow, 1933.

Ref: White, "Some Glasgow Designers and Their Work," ill.; *Ver Sacrum,* IV (1901), p. 396 ill.

FRANCE

Le beau est toujours bizarre.
                                    Charles Baudelaire

L'Art, c'est la liberté, le luxe, l'efflorescence,
c'est l'épanouissement de l'âme dans l'oisiveté.
                                    Théophile Gautier

Mais l'illustration, c'est la décoration d'un livre!
... une broderie d'arabesques sur les pages, un
accompagnement de lignes expressives.
                                    Maurice Denis

48

Histoire des Quatre Fils Aymon
Eugène Grasset, illustrator
Paris, H. Launette, 1883

Decorated title, border ornaments and vignettes by Grasset printed in multi-color "chromotypogravure."

11 x 8¾ in. Pictorial wrappers by Grasset printed in brown, tan, black, blue and gold, with red and black lettering on buff paper. Black morocco, bound by Marius-Michel with vertical insert panel of brown calf incised with trophy design signed with initials *HMM*, lettered in gold; doublures with mosaic in red, brown and tan morocco, with panel and guards of green and tan brocade, edges gilt. No. 195 of "tirage de luxe" of 200 numbered copies printed on china. Edition of 200 copies (100 on imperial japan, 100 on *papier de chine*).

Gift of Philip Hofer

The *Histoire des Quatre Fils Aymon* is one of the seminal forerunners of Art Nouveau book design in France, perhaps the first illustrated book in which text and illustration were conceived as a coordinated mise en page, one complementing and integrating with the other to the extent that Grasset's pictorial borders not only surround the pages of type, but often serve as a muted background over which the type is printed. The story derives from Renaud de Montauban's popular edition of the legendary story of Charlemagne. Grasset's decorations combine pictorial images of the Middle Ages intermixed with strong doses of Celtic and Japanese ornament. This Celtic and Medieval style survived in Grasset's illustration for another epic: Gaston Paris, *Aventures Merveilleuses de Huon de Bordeaux* published in 1898. In the early titles Grasset is employing the lettering developed into the famous "Grasset typeface" widely used throughout the Nineties. Charles Gillot, the first photoengraver in Paris, asked his friend Grasset to illustrate the *Histoire des Quatre Fils Aymon* in chromolithography, a reproductive process in the production of which Gillot exercised fastidious care.

Ref: Madsen, *Art Noveau,* p. 94 ill.; Uzanne, "Eugène Grasset and Decorative Art in France," p. 37-42 ill.; Uzanne, *L'Art dans la Décoration des Livres,* p. 9 ill.; Abdy, *The French Poster,* p. 115; New York, The Museum of Modern Art, *Art Nouveau,* no. 117, p. 170 ill.; p. 39.

49

Eugène Grasset, *La Plante et ses Applications Ornamentales*
Eugène Grasset, illustrator
Paris, Librairie des Beaux Arts, E. Lévy, 1897.
2 volumes.

Title-page, 72 numbered color lithographs in each volume after watercolors by Grasset. Drawn and signed in the stone by 11 different draughtsmen.

18 x 13 in. Half maroon calf, marbled boards. This copy formerly from library of Cyrus McCormick.

Gift of John Goelet

Christopher Dresser's *Rudiments of Botany,* 1859, was one of the first influential books to apply the theory of plant form to decorative arts. In the last quarter of the nineteenth century a whole flood of pattern books appeared with plants as the principal motifs. Grasset, by juxtaposing accurate illustrations of individual plants with geometricised and stylized adaptations for use in the applied arts, promulgates his theory that a return to the direct study of nature is the only true source of comprehension of ornamental motifs. The plates, executed by his pupils and brilliantly printed under the supervision of Emile Lévy, are strong in pattern and color, appropriate for wallpaper, fabric and ceramic as well as applied metalwork.

Ref: Schmutzler, *Art Nouveau,* p. 101; Madsen, *Art Nouveau,* p. 53; Gustave Soulier, "La Plante et ses Applications Ornamentales," p. 187-189 ill.

50

Eugène Grasset, *Les Mois, douze compositions*
Eugène Grasset, illustrator
Paris, G. de Malherbe, n.d.

FEVRIER

50. Eugène Grasset.
Février. Watercolor
for *Les Mois*. n.d.

12 full-page illustrations by Grasset for each of the twelve months engraved on wood and printed in color on china paper, signed in the block *EG*, one by the engraver Boileau. This copy with 12 original preparatory drawings by Grasset, in pencil, pen and watercolor on wove paper, signed *EG*; 1 etched portrait of Grasset.

12⁵⁄₁₆ x 9½ in. Brown morocco bound by Marius-Michel, upper cover inlaid in green and purple morocco with waving orchid plants; doublures paneled in green moiré, top edges gilt. Original gray wrappers bound in, with printed title and typographic ornament.

Lent by Raphael Esmerian

This series of decorative calendar pages is a lady's book à la mode with comely maidens dressed in "aesthetic" free-flowing costumes joyfully tending their well-ordered, full-flowering gardens. Grasset shows himself here more as an illustrator than a flamboyant stylist or theorist. These garden settings are a foil for his sense of formalized surface pattern, showing the influence of Walter Crane. In his *Méthode de composition ornamentale* published in 1904 Grasset wrote: "Every curve gives the idea of movement and life . . . the line of the curve should be full, rounded, closed and harmonious like a stalk of young sap."

Ref: Hofstätter, *Jugendstil Druckkunst*, p. 44.

51
Emile Zola, *Le Rêve*
Carlos Schwabe and *Lucien Métivet,* illustrators
Paris, Librairie Marpon et Flammarion [1892]

Title-page with wood-engraved vignette by Lucien Métivet; 26 full-page wood-engravings by Carlos Schwabe and 6 by Métivet, some signed in block *Carlos Schwabe* and dated *1891, 1892,* or with initials *LM,* some with initials of cutter, *WH*; borders, chapter headings, and tailpieces. Printed by Marpon & Flammarion; cover printed by Hérold & Cie. in color.

First copy: 11 ⅛ x 7½ in. Extra-illustrated copy, with watercolor by H. P. Dillon, watercolor by Schwabe on Whatman paper for illustration opp. p. 264; 2 etched author portraits. No. 12 of 30 copies on japan, numbered and paraphed by the publisher. Original pictorial wrappers, upper cover with title and symbolic design of village by Schwabe, signed *Carlos Schwabe* and dated *1891,* lower cover with bust of female figure; extra wrappers printed on silk. Olive-green morocco, upper cover with multi-color inserted calf panel with incised and mosaic design of female figure, clouds, lilies, and sunflowers, lower cover with inserted rose calf panel with incised and mosaic design of symbols of Christ's Passion in brown and gold. Edges silvered, red and green olive morocco doublures inlaid with white, green, brown, and ochre lily plant, thorn border, holly leaves and daisies. Binding executed by Charles Meunier, signed on upper cover with initials *CM '98,* on inner cover *Ch. Meunier, 1898.* Cover guard and slipcase in brown morocco.

Lent by Raphael Esmerian

Second copy: 11 x 7⅜ in. One of regular edition on holland. Half blue morocco, gilt-tooled with geometric leaf design, spine with inlaid design of symbols of Christ's Passion, in red and black, marbled board sides, by *de Samblancx-Weckesser,* stamped on flyleaf.

Bequest of Edward Ray Thompson

Carlos Schwabe, a Swiss painter-engraver who dominates this first illustrated edition of Zola's *Le Rêve,* also illustrated Baudelaire, *Les Fleurs du Mal* (1900). His highly charged Neo-Gothic design for the pictorial wrapper with a white dove enveloping in his wings the cathedral and medieval town, and the heavy vapor rising from the scented passion flowers below, effusively conveys the veiled and mystic symbolism of the supernatural content of this novel. Paris in the Nineties was alive with psychical experiments, particularly Rosicrucianism, which found expression in the literary-artistic world.

Ref: Vicaire, vol. 7, p. 1213; Victoria and Albert Museum, *Mackintosh* cat., no. 44.

51. Carlos Schwabe.
Cover for *Le Rêve*. 1892

52

Claude Debussy, *La Damoiselle Elue, Poème Lyrique, d'après D.-G. Rossetti*
Gabriel Sarrazin, translator
Maurice Denis, illustrator
Dedicated to Paul Dukas
Paris, Librairie de l'Art Indépendant, 1893

Unillustrated. Printed by Delanchy & Cie.

14¼ x 9¼ in. Cream wrappers, upper cover printed with color lithograph of "La damoiselle élue" by Maurice Denis, signed with initials *MAUD* and with monogram.
No. 53 of 125 copies on white wove paper. Edition of 160 copies (4 on china paper, 8 on Whatman, 8 on imperial japan, 15 on holland, 125 on white wove).

Purchased from the bequest of Amy Lowell

The legacy of Dante Gabriel Rossetti as both artist and author is apparent among the French Symbolists, and this transformation of "The Blessed Damozel" indicates his influence on two of the most important French figures. The early work of Maurice Denis is among the first and most complete graphic expressions of Art Nouveau. In addition to this cover and the illustrations for André Gide's *Le Voyage d'Urien* (No. 53) of 1893, he had made a lithographic frontispiece for Edouard Dujardin's *Réponse de la Bergère au Berger* in 1892. Debussy's music was highly regarded by the audience responsive to new artistic experiments, and the composer himself played this composition in Brussels in 1894 for the opening of "La Libre Esthétique."

Ref: Madsen, *Art Nouveau,* p. 31; Guignard, "Les Livres Illustrés de Maurice Denis," p. 51 ill.

53

André Gide, *Le Voyage d'Urien*
Maurice Denis, illustrator
Paris, Librairie de l'Art Indépendant, 1893

30 lithographs by Maurice Denis, one signed *MAUD* in the stone. Lithographs printed by Edward Ancourt in black and yellow and black and green; text printed by Paul Schmidt.

First copy: 8 x 7⅜ in. Red-brown morocco, bound by Lortic Fils, edges gilt. Unique copy on japan. Edition of 302 copies (1 on japan, 1 on china, 300 regular). This copy inscribed on preliminary leaf: *heu! heu! quam pingui macer est mihi taurus in ervo. André Gide.*

Bequest of Harold Wilmerding Bell

Second copy: 8 x 7½ in. Original cream wrappers. Proof copy before text.

Gift of Philip Hofer

Third copy: 8 x 7½ in. Original cream wrappers, with dedication on half-title: *à Oscar Wilde / en hommage / André Gide.*

Lent by Philip Hofer

André Gide inscribed a copy of *Le Voyage d'Urien* to Denis at the time of its first issue: "Ce voyage vraiement fait ensemble." Gide wrote his *Voyage* under the influence of Symbolism. The Symbolist poets and writers were searching for "fluidity," a word they constantly used, and rhythm and division into rhythmical units were the prime ingredients of their poetic form. The visual vocabulary of Denis was also infused with fluidity and rhythm and thus in harmony with Gide's text, even if not surpassing it, as Gide feared when he inscribed this copy with the phrase from Virgil: "Alas! Alas! how thin is my bull in the fat vetch." In a sense these illustrations are precursors of the relaxed sensuality of the "Luxe, calme et volupté" paintings and sketches of Matisse (1904–05), although to this Denis would not have agreed.
This is the only book by Denis in which the illustrations were drawn directly on the stone by the artist.

Ref: Boston Museum-Harvard College Library, *The Artist and the Book,* no. 76, p. 58; Garvey, "Art Nouveau and the French Book of the Eighteen-Nineties," p. 381-382 ill.; Madsen, *Art Nouveau,* p. 98.

La damoiselle élue

52. Maurice Denis. Cover for
La Damoiselle Elue. 1893

XIX

Voix de l'Orgueil: un cri puissant comme d'un cor,
Des étoiles de sang sur des cuirasses d'or.
On trébuche à travers des chaleurs d'incendie...
Mais en somme la voix s'en va, comme d'un cor.

Voix de la Haine: cloche en mer, fausse, assourdie
De neige lente. Il fait si froid! Lourde, affadie,
La vie a peur et court follement sur le quai,
Loin de la cloche qui devient plus assourdie.

Voix de la Chair: un gros tapage fatigué.
Des gens ont bu. L'endroit fait semblant d'être gai.
Des yeux, des noms, et l'air plein de parfums atroces
Où vient mourir le gros tapage fatigué.

Voix d'Autrui: des lointains dans des brouillards. Des noces
Vont et viennent. Des tas d'embarras. Des négoces,
Et tout le cirque des civilisations
Au son trotte-menu du violon des noces.

SAGESSE

54
Paul Verlaine, *Sagesse*
Maurice Denis, illustrator
Paris, Ambroise Vollard, 1911

Title-page with wood-engraved vignette, 72 wood-engravings, 1 vignette by Maurice Denis; 3 signed with initials *MD*, 2 signed *Mau. D.* in the block. Blocks cut and printed by Jacques Beltrand in black, brown, gray, or green, title-page in red and black.

11¼ x 9⅛ in. Cream board portfolio, title in red, blue morocco title label on spine. No. 9 of 40 copies on japan with extra suite of wood-engravings hand-colored by the artist. Edition of 250 copies (40 on japan with extra suite, 210 on holland).

Gift of Philip Hofer

Denis drew these illustrations, his first, in 1889 and exhibited them with the Indépendants in 1891, where their influence was considerable, although they were not published for twenty years. With or without benefit of the hand-colored "extra suite," the wood-engravings which decorate these pages speak for the Art Nouveau style at its most lyrical. The illustrations mark a decided break with nineteenth-century narrative style in their asymmetry, flatness and expressive intensity. The restraint with which the curvilinear designs match the verses of Verlaine must not be interpreted as over-simplification. Denis is at his subtlest and best here — instinctively dependent upon Gauguin, he is nevertheless an individual designer.

Ref: Lewis, *The Twentieth Century Book,* p. 9; Boston Museum-Harvard College Library, *The Artist and the Book,* no. 77, p. 59.

55
Victor Joze, pseud., *Reine de Joie*
Pierre Bonnard, designer of cover, *Henri de Toulouse-Lautrec,* illustrator
Paris, Henri Julien, 1892

Frontispiece reduced reproduction of lithographic poster for *Reine de Joie* by Toulouse-Lautrec (Delteil 342, Mack 283 f.).

7¼ x 4½ in. White wrappers with continuous upper and lower lithographed cover design by Pierre Bonnard of Japanese-style figures in black and color, signed in the stone lower right with monogram *PBf.* Dedication copy signed in pen: *A Romain Coolus / cordialement, / Victor Joze.*

Lent by Philip Hofer

Victor Joze (pseudonym for the Polish writer Joze Dobrski de Jastzebiec) was a friend and neighbor of Toulouse-Lautrec, and *Reine de Joie, moeurs du demi-monde* is part of his series *La Ménagerie*

Sociale. Lautrec designed another poster, used on the cover of Joze's *Babylone d'Allemagne,* 1893, as well as a cover for his *La Tribu d'Isidore,* 1897. Lautrec's designs appear in several books and programs of the Nineties: Romain Coolus, playwright, wrote a story *Le Bon Jockey,* 1895, illustrated by Lautrec; in 1896 he contributed lithographic portraits to the double program for Wilde's *Salomé* and Coolus' *Raphael,* then playing at the Théatre de L'Oeuvre. Bonnard's design for *Reine de Joie* is a mixture of the figurative and the abstract; the bobbing black Japanese silhouettes move in sinuous rhythm with the colored figures.

Ref: Terrasse, *Bonnard,* p. 189, no. 3; Garvey, "Art Nouveau and the French Book of the Eighteen-Nineties," p. 380 ill.; Julien, *Les Affiches de Toulouse-Lautrec,* p. 94; Albi-Paris, *Centenaire de Toulouse-Lautrec,* no. 174 ill.

56

Claude Terrasse, *Petit Solfège Illustré*
Pierre Bonnard, illustrator
Paris, Librairies-Imprimeries Réunies, Ancienne Maison Quantin, 1893

30 lithographed page decorations by Bonnard. Printed by Allier père et fils, Grenoble, in color.

8⅞ x 11¼ in. Oblong brown boards, upper cover with lithograph in black by Bonnard of title and children singing; lower cover with lithograph of mother and child with music book, signed *PB 1893.* One of *premier tirage* of limited edition on Japanese vellum. This copy with autograph signature of François Fosca on flyleaf.

Purchased from the Caroline Miller Parker Fund

The *Petit Solfège* and *Petites scènes familières pour piano* by Claude Terrasse are early music albums illustrated by Bonnard. The *Solfège* is a beginner's music instruction book with practice scales and do-ré-mi catechism. Bonnard's borders help to defray the pupil's boredom, their impish humor an avid accomplice to the reluctant renegade.

Ref: Carteret, vol. 4, p. 77.

57

André Mellerio, *La Lithographie Originale en Couleurs*
Pierre Bonnard, illustrator
Paris, L'Estampe et l'Affiche, 1898

Frontispiece lithograph on china paper by Bonnard. Printed by the Société Typographique, Chateaudun, with lithograph in color.

8½ x 8 in. Buff wrappers, upper cover with color lithograph by Bonnard of a woman standing by a lithographic stone examining a proof.
No. 172 of 200 numbered copies on holland. Edition of 1000 copies (200 on holland, 800 on Japanese vellum). Presentation copy signed in ink on half-title: *A Monsieur Le Roux / Cet essai d'art — en Hommage de sincère gratitude / André Mellerio.*

Gift of Philip Hofer

Bonnard decorated his book covers in broad, deceptively haphazard designs with imbalanced brush lettering splashed across the page. The cover for the *Album de la Revue Blanche* (1895) is a strong example of this informal silhouette style, while the early cover for *La Reine de Joie* (1892) and *Petit Solfège* (1893) are early examples (Nos. 55, 56). Mellerio characterizes Bonnard as a "gray painter, fond of purplish, russet, somber tones." He notes his "shrewd observation, his impish gaiety . . . a curious line in movement, of a monkeylike suppleness. . . ."

Ref: Rewald, *Pierre Bonnard,* p. 30.

58

Gustave Geffroy, *Yvette Guilbert*
Henri de Toulouse-Lautrec, illustrator
Paris, L'Estampe Originale, 1894

16 lithographs of Yvette Guilbert by Henri de Toulouse-Lautrec, signed with monogram *TL.* Printed by Edward Ancourt (lithographs) and by Typographie Frémont (text) in olive-green.

15 x 15 in. Cream boards with ties, upper cover stamped in black with title and design of Yvette

Guilbert's gloves by Toulouse-Lautrec, signed with monogram *TL*.
No. 40 of 100 copies.

Lent by Philip Hofer

The silhouettes of the entertainers Yvette Guilbert and Jane Avril were heightened and dramatized by Lautrec into expressive, curvilinear outlines that are the essence of Art Nouveau. They both appeared in his 1892 poster *Divan Japonais* and again in his illustrations for Georges Montorgueil's *Le Café Concert* of 1893. In the *Yvette Guilbert* volume, square in format, only the recto sides of the leaves are printed. Each one depicts the singer in a different pose, her restless gestures breaking the narrow composition and stabbing into the text itself. The cover design with the sinuous silhouette of the famous black gloves (which have been called "hieroglyphs of decadence") and powder puff tossed nonchalantly on the tiered shelving of a dressing table is an astonishing tour de force.

Ref: Delteil, vol. 10, no. 79-95; Wick, *Yvette Guilbert*.

59

Jules Renard, *Histoires Naturelles*
Henri de Toulouse-Lautrec, illustrator
Paris, H. Floury, 1899

22 lithographs by Toulouse-Lautrec signed with monogram *HTL*. Lithographs printed by Henry Stern; text printed by Ch. Renaudie.

12 x 8¾ in. Buff wrappers, lithographed title and design of fox in black by Toulouse-Lautrec signed with monogram *HTL*. Blue-green morocco inlaid with horizontal band of black and ochre; upper cover, onlaid in white, black and red morocco and incised with swan design after Lautrec; lower cover onlaid with rooster; doublures with white morocco panel inlaid and incised with guinea hens and turkeys, front and back respectively; white moiré guards, spattered silver endpapers, edges gilt; half morocco cover guard and slip case. No. 35 of 100 numbered copies.

Gift of Philip Hofer

Renard wrote in his Journal: "Descaves wants to persuade me that I shall need fifty *Histoires Naturelles* to make a volume. It isn't his opinion alone; others share it. Lautrec suggests that he illustrate eight of them and that we sell a hundred copies at 25 francs apiece. We would share the profit." Renard's inspiration came from his country home, Chitry, and the artist Toulouse-Lautrec also had his memories of nostalgic farmyard friends. But both author and artist visited constantly the Jardin d'Acclimatation and the Jardin des Plantes. "Quelquefois une image qui semble née à la campagne vient en réalité de Paris." So subtle and delicate is Toulouse-Lautrec's approach to these animals that at times one overlooks the Art Nouveau elements in the designs. They are strikingly evident in the cover design with its bold lettering and the curving silhouette of the fox.

Ref: Guichard, *L'Oeuvre et L'Ame de Jules Renard*, p. 198-212; Bogan and Roget, *The Journal of Jules Renard*, p. 74.

60

Edmond Haraucourt, *L'Effort*
Léon Rudnicki, Eugène Courboin, Alexandre Lunois, Carlos Schwabe, Alexandre Séon, illustrators
Paris, Les Bibliophiles Contemporains, 1894

Pictorial title, half-title and frontispiece lithographed in colored floral design by Rudnicki, signed in the stone *Leon Rudnicki*.

Part I: *La Madone*: 18 color lithographs by Alexandre Lunois, 1 signed *Alex. Lunois '93*.
Lithographs printed by LaFontaine; text printed on the handpress of L'Ancienne Maison Quantin.
Part II: *L'Antéchrist*: 38 compositions in color by Eugène Courboin, signed in the plates *Eug. Courboin* and *Rougeron-Vignerot sc*. Color printing by A. Charpentier; text and blocks printed on the handpress of L'Ancienne Maison Quantin.
Part III: *L'Immortalité*: 32 compositions by Carlos Schwabe, those in color signed *Carlos Schwabe '93* and *Gillot sc.*, the 10 in black and white etched by Auguste Massé. Color printing by A. Charpentier; text printed on the handpress of L'Ancienne Maison Quantin.

60. Léon Rudnicki. Cover for *L'Effort*. 1894

Part IV: *La Fin du Monde*: decorated with 46 symbolic drawings by Alexandre Séon, printed in black, some signed *L. Bordier sc., Chelet sc.,* etc.; frontispiece printed in gold signed *Alex. SEON*. Drawings engraved by Michelet & Bordier and printed on the handpress of L'Ancienne Maison Quantin.

11⅛ x 8½ in. Cream wrappers decorated upper and lower covers with multi-color floral designs in lithograph by Rudnicki, signed in the stone *Leon Rudnicki '94*; spine with thistle design; silk brocade cover guard. No. 121 (copy of Charles-Edward Pratt) of 180 copies on special paper watermarked Edmond Haraucourt and with floral borders; paper designed by Octave Uzanne and executed by Mazure et Perrigot.

Bequest of Mrs. Harriet J. Bradbury

Edmond Haraucourt belonged to the Parnassian aftermath. In 1890 he had published *La Passion, un mystère*. *L'Effort*, published for Les Sociétaires de l'Académie des Beaux Livres, was one of the most ambitious, lavish and costly collaborations of French bookmaking in the Nineties. Five artists contributed, numerous wood-engravers, printers and technicians. The fine hand of the savant-bibliophile Octave Uzanne, with his insatiable taste for deluxe editions and fine bindings, was close to this production, for it was he who designed the watermarked paper. It would take several copies of this book to exhibit it comprehensively, but the cover and introductory titles by Léon Rudnicki and Part III, *L'Immortalité*, illustrated by Carlos Schwabe with refined floral borders, are the most striking contribution. In the other border illustrations there is an element of rather vapid mysticism, symbolism and transcendentalism that seems more humorous than inspired today. Like most mass collaborations the book lacks unity of spirit, however fine in its technical execution.

Ref: Carteret, vol. 4, p. 198.

61

Jean Lorrain, pseud., *Ma Petite Ville*
Léon Rudnicki, illustrator and designer of binding;

Manuel Orazi, illustrator
Paris, Société Française d'Editions d'Art, 1898

Title and 5 wood-engraved vignettes designed by Rudnicki, signed *Léon Rudnicki* and *RVD. sc.*; 6 full-page illustrations and 4 head- and tailpieces etched in color by Frédéric Massé after watercolors by Manuel Orazi, signed *Frédéric Massé*. Printed by Edouard Crété, Corbeil; etchings printed by Monsieur Taneur, hand-colored by Monsieur Saudé.

9¾ x 7 in. Buff japan wrappers printed in gold, upper and lower covers with repeat floral design by Rudnicki, signed lower right *LR*. No. 157 of 250 numbered copies on *vélin à la cuve de Rives*. Edition: 300 copies (50 on *japon impérial*, 250 on *vélin*).

Lent by John D. Merriam

Jean Lorrain was a minor but fervent Symbolist in his writing, a biting critic in his literary journalism. This book bears the subtitle *Le Miracle de Bretagne, Un Veuvage d'Amour,* no doubt referring to his birthplace of Fécamp. The cover design in gold is the must successful contribution to this book.

Ref: Talvert et Place, *Bibliographie*, vol. 12, p. 236.

62

Octave Uzanne, *L'Art dans la Décoration Extérieure des Livres en France et à l'Etranger*
Léon Rudnicki, Richard Wallace, illustrators;
Louis Rhead, designer of cover
Paris, Société Française d'Editions d'Art, L-Henry May, 1898

Title-page, half-title, 20 vignettes, foliated initials by Léon Rudnicki, signed with artist's name and initials *RVD. sc.*; frontispiece by Richard Wallace, signed with artist's name; numerous reproductions of cover and binding designs. Printed by La Maison Lahure, 1897, with title-page, frontispiece, and description of edition in red and black.

10¾ x 8 in. Multi-color wrappers, upper cover printed with title in red, figure of woman in yellow holding book and standing against blue tree by Louis Rhead, lower cover with blue tree, books and printing press by Louis Rhead, signed *Louis* on upper cover. Bound in contemporary mottled red-brown calf, upper cover gilt-stamped in stylized foliate design with gilt title in recessed panel, lower cover with diaper pattern of foliage, signed *Alfred Bookbinder,* with green silk doublures.
One of 1000 regular copies. Edition of 1060 copies (60 on japan, 1000 regular).

Purchased from the Caroline Miller Parker Fund

Uzanne's book, with its many reproductions, gives a picture of book cover and binding design in the Nineties. He illustrated work by Walter Crane, Charles Ricketts, Lucien Pissarro, Gleeson White, Aubrey Beardsley, and Cobden-Sanderson among the English; Eugène Grasset, George Auriol, Jules Chéret, Carlos Schwabe, and Alphonse Mucha among the French.

63
Edmond Rostand, *La Princesse Lointaine*
Dedicated to Madame Sarah Bernhardt
Paris, G. Charpentier et E. Fasquelle, 1895

Unillustrated. Printed by Imprimeries Réunies

7¾ x 4⅞ in. Ivory levant morocco, jewelled, bound for Sarah Bernhardt, upper cover with lily plant on stalk appliqué in gilt-bronze and pavé diamonds and topaz; gilt-bronze clasp in tracery design set with colored stones and large cabochon amethyst; lower cover appliqué in gilt-bronze with monogram *SB* and *Quand Même*; blue silk lining, top edges silver-gilt. No. 10 of 15 numbered copies on japan with blue wrappers bound in.

Lent by Raphael Esmerian

This is a first edition of *La Princesse Lointaine,* a play in four acts by the young Rostand, a gentle prelude to *Cyrano de Bergerac.* The play "offers a striking example of romanticism, tempered by the more staid ways of the Parnassians, and diversified with wilful riming oddities à la Banville, while here and there appears a bit of 'decadence' or 'symbolism' in the form of a defective cesura."
As Mélissinde, princesse d'Orient, comtesse de Tripoli, Sarah Bernhardt was the far-famed impersonator of the leading role. The dedication inscribed in the flyleaf à *Madame Sarah Bernhardt* was written from London, Savoy Hotel, 17 June:

Je suis parti, non pas vers Tripoli, mais vers
Le pays cher à Monsieur Taine,
Pour encore une fois les entendre, mes vers,
Dits par ma Princesse Lointaine!

Comme Rudel, pour voir les magiques palais
Que votre voix, clef d'or, nous ouvre,
J'ai voulu m'embarquer! Et j'ai pris à Calais
Une Nef qui partait pour Douvre.

J'aurais voulu braver mieux que le mal de mer,
Et voguer au moins jusqu'à l'Inde,
Pour vous prouver, Sarah, combien il m'était cher
De réentendre Mélissinde!

Car on mourrait, ainsi que votre Prince-Amant,
Pour la jouissance d'esthète
De voir, entre les lys énormes, lentement,
Tourner votre petite tête.

Ref: Rostand, *La Princesse Lointaine,* New York, 1899, Intro. Cf. this cat. No. 67.

64
Georges Rodenbach, *Les Vierges*
Joseph Rippl-Rónai, illustrator
Paris, S. Bing, 1895

4 color lithographs by Joseph Rippl-Rónai. Printed by Chamerot and Renouard.

9⅞ x 6¾ in. Modern half citron morocco, figured board sides and end papers, top edges gilt. Copy on japan.

Purchased from the Caroline Miller Parker Fund

The imprint of S. Bing on the colophon page of *Les Vierges* points to a man now recognized as a pioneer in the dissemination of the Art Nouveau style.

Samuel Bing was a German with experience in the manufacture of ceramics. His interests led him to the Orient, and his Parisian shop, "L'Art Nouveau Bing," not only helped to propagate the Japanese taste in France, but also the new style itself in various media, including books. Work by the Nabis was prominently on view at "L'Art Nouveau Bing," including that of the Hungarian Rippl-Rónai. *Les Vierges* is delicately and somewhat archaically conceived and carefully carried out, with the plates and text printed on one side only of folded and unopened leaves. There is no title-page, but a colophon stating: "Ce petit livre, imaginé par deux amis: Joseph Rippl-Rónai et James Pitcairn-Knowles, au temps de la fête de Noël, en l'année 1895, a paru sous la bonne protection de M. S. Bing à Paris." Pitcairn-Knowles, born in Rotterdam of Scottish parents, illustrated with woodcuts a companion to this little book, Rodenbach's *Les Tombeaux*. These illustrations are "Nabis" in spirit reflecting not only the Brittany period of Gauguin and Emil Bernard, but very much the decorative linear rhythm of Maurice Denis. Rodenbach, Belgian poet and novelist, did much with Verhaeren and Maeterlinck to extend the Symbolist movement.

Ref: Weisberg, "Samuel Bing," p. 298-299 ill.; Hofstätter, *Jugendstil Druckkunst,* p. 260-261.

65

Maurice Maeterlinck, *Douze Chansons*
Charles Doudelet, illustrator
Paris, P.-V. Stock, 1896

12 pictorial woodcuts and 12 vignettes by Charles Doudelet, some signed with monogram *CD* in a circle. Printed by Louis van Melle, Ghent.

9½ x 12½ in. Green wrappers, upper cover stamped with title in black and design of floral ornaments in orange by Doudelet.
One of 600 copies.

The Rilke collection of Richard von Mises.
Purchased from the Amy Lowell Fund

The Belgian Symbolists Maeterlinck and Doudelet were both widely published in other countries of western Europe, particularly France, and Doudelet's illustrations for the German magazine *Pan* helped to influence the new style in Berlin. In the large narrative illustrations of the *Douze Chansons,* his interest in Italian Renaissance composition and perspective is most apparent. In the flat and curvilinear details of some of these scenes, however, and in the little vignettes, Doudelet's own decorative style of the Nineties breaks through these conventions.

Ref: Schmutzler, *Art Nouveau,* p. 54, fig. 43 ill.

66

André Mellerio, *Le Mouvement Idéaliste en Peinture*
Henri Nocq, illustrator and designer of cover, *Odilon Redon,* illustrator
Paris, H. Floury, 1896

Frontispiece lithograph by Redon, signed lower right in stone with monogram *OR*; 28 wood-engraved chapter headings designed by Henri Nocq. Printed by the Imprimerie Darantière, Dijon.

7⅞ x 5½ in. Chestnut-brown wrappers with abstract cactus design by Nocq printed in dark brown, signed left center *HN*; lower cover with printed device and monogram *CR*. One of regular edition on wove paper. There was also a small edition on holland with the Redon lithograph on japan.

Gift of Peter A. Wick

Henri Nocq, a goldsmith, medallist and architect, designed this cover, a flat pattern which seems to grow in random fashion across the surface like a wayward cactus plant. Redon's single lithograph, a human head held captive by a serpent arm, is followed by twenty-eight chapter headings, some floral and some abstract and sinuous in the Art Nouveau manner. In Mellerio's essay he presents the thesis that four artists have contributed to the *mouvement idéaliste* in painting: Puvis de Chavannes, Gustave Moreau, Odilon Redon and Paul Gauguin. Other essays are devoted to Toulouse-Lautrec, Ibels, Bonnard, Roussel and Denis.

Ref: Mellerio, *Odilon Redon,* cat. no. 159.

67

Robert de Flers, *Ilsée, Princesse de Tripoli*
Alphonse Mucha, illustrator
Paris, L'Edition d'Art, H. Piazza & Cie., 1897

Decorated lithographic title-page by Mucha, printed in red-brown, yellow and gray; pictorial frontispiece and 130 lithographs in color by Mucha, including the cover, 10 foliated initials, fleurons and culs-de-lampe. Watermarked *motif d'estampage* of lily on opening leaf executed by Alex. Charpentier. Lithographs printed on the hand press by L'Imprimerie Champenois; text printed on the hand press of L'Edition d'Art. Medici type designed especially for this edition by S. Berthier & Durey.

12⁹⁄₁₆ x 9½ in. Original dark green wrappers with lily border printed in green and gold. Green oasis morocco bound by Roger Powell (1969), inlaid with five shades of morocco, blocked in blind after frieze designs by Mucha, gold-tooled, top edges gilt. Original green and gold covers bound in. No. 155 of 180 numbered examples on *vélin à la forme*. Edition: 252 copies (1 on parchment, 1 on satin, 35 on japan, 35 on china, 180 on *vélin*). Special watermarked paper made by Les Papeteries d'Arches.

Gift of John Goelet

Alphonse Mucha, the toast of two continents in the Nineties, is best known for his posters of Sarah Bernhardt. In 1896 Mucha had designed the sets and costumes for Rostand's *La Princesse Lointaine,* an immediate success. The artist was approached by the publisher Piazza to illustrate an edition of the play and signed a contract for this assignment. Rostand's demands were such that he never came to terms with the publisher, whereupon Piazza engaged Robert, Marquis de Flers to rewrite the old legend on which Rostand had based his play. Mucha moved to a new studio near the Val de Grâce, installed lithographic presses and set to work. The work on *Ilsée* proceeded as follows: "the script which had been made for me from the proofs of the book was divided into separate pages and I sketched the composition for each of them in pencil on tracing paper. Then I drew the figural part on to the

block which I passed to the lithographers who completed the page, following my pencilled rough. As soon as the block was finished, it went to the print shop and straight on to the press. Thus, for at least six weeks, my studio was converted into a lithographic workshop with all its inconveniences."
The character of this book is in the spirit of Grasset's *Histoire des Quatre Fils Aymon* (No. 48), another *chanson de geste,* with the opulent Slavic overtones of Mucha's Czech heritage. The title-page with cusped arch motif and Arabic tracery sets the stage for this deluxe edition. An edition in German was published in Prague in 1901. Cf. No. 63.

Ref: Carteret, vol. 4, p. 162; Talvert et Place, vol. 6, p. 61; Mucha, *Alphonse Mucha,* p. 89-104 ill.; Reade, *Art Nouveau and Alphonse Mucha,* p. 10-11 ill.; *La Plume,* p. 24-37 ill.

68

Marcel Schwob, *La Porte des Rêves*
Georges de Feure, illustrator; *Octave Uzanne,* artistic director
Dedicated to Samuel Pozzi of the Academy of Medicine
Paris, Les Bibliophiles Indépendants, chez Henry Floury, 1899

Frontispiece triptych etched in two tones and hand-colored, signed *de Feure*; 16 full-page wood-engravings in black and white signed in the block; 32 border designs printed in variant tones and signed; 15 culs-de-lampe. Printed by A. Lahure, Paris.

11⅜ x 8¾ in. Printed floral wrappers, upper cover with vignette and decorative title in dark blue by de Feure, lower cover with lettered vignette in blue. No. 21 (copy for G. Deladerière) of 200 copies on japan. Edition of 200 copies (5 with 12 original drawings by de Feure, 195 regular).

Marcel Schwob was associated with the early days of the Symbolist *Mercure de France.* His imaginative tales are often ornate and morbid, with a strange mixture of reality and fantasy. His career was cut short by an operation in 1895, which may explain the dedication here to Dr. Pozzi:

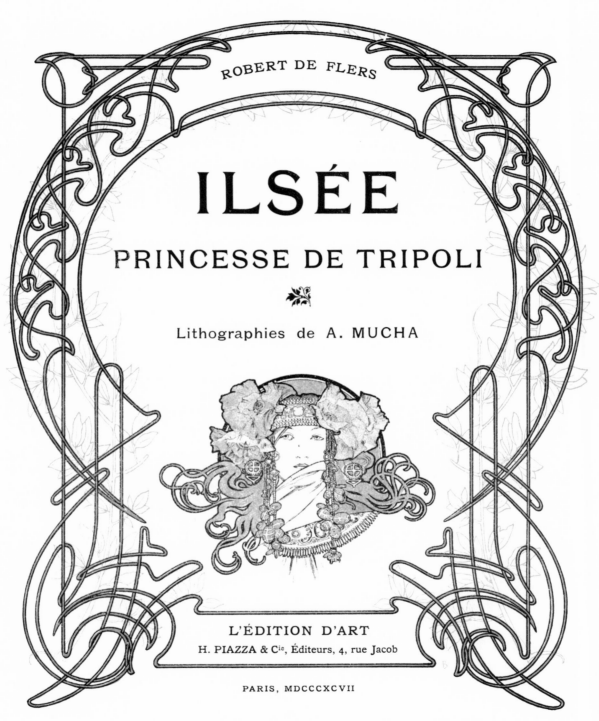

ROBERT DE FLERS

ILSÉE

PRINCESSE DE TRIPOLI

Lithographies de A. MUCHA

L'ÉDITION D'ART

H. PIAZZA & Cie, Éditeurs, 4, rue Jacob

PARIS, MDCCCXCVII

67. Alphonse Mucha. Title-page for *Ilsée, Princesse de Tripoli.* 1897

"My dear Doctor

"The Ancients believed that two doors opened on the dark kingdom of Erebus; one light, allows to escape among us wingèd thoughts; the other, massive, imprisoning forever those who have crossed over.

"I had descended to the threshold of the inexorable door. You had seized me with your hand 'which cures everything it touches,' and you led me back towards the sun.

"Thanks to you I have been able to dream these dreams. They are given to you as a feeble testimony of my eternal gratitude."

De Feure became the leading exponent of French Art Nouveau. He worked as a painter and furniture designer, and his posters were exhibited far and wide. His graceful, fastidious and almost feminine style is a leit-motiv of the *belle époque*. Up to 1900 his form language derived from plant forms and flowers, evident in these decorative borders, which he here endeavors to imbue less with pretty images than with sombre, mysterious grotesques linking organic and animal forms.

Ref: Madsen, *Art Nouveau*, p. 145-146; Uzanne, "On the Drawings of M. Georges de Feure"; Hofstätter, *Jugendstil Druckkunst*, p. 50.

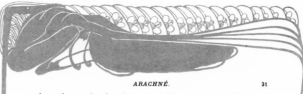

69

Hector Guimard, *Le Castel Béranger*
Introduction by G. D. Hostingue
Hector Guimard, designer
Paris, Librairie Rouam et Cie., 1899

Title-page by Guimard with decorated cartouche printed in aqua, green and pink, lettered in red and dark blue, signed lower right with monogram *HG* and lower left *V. Lelong sc.*; 65 color plates of plans, elevations and photographic details of this architectural project, signed with monogram *HG*. The plates executed after the photographic negatives of Eug. Voisin by Fortier-Marotte, and printed in watercolor facsimile by M. J. Saudé under the author's direction. Wove paper specially printed by Grosvenor, Chater & Co. Text printed by Chamerot et Renouard.

12½ x 17 in. Oblong portfolio in green boards with upper cover designed by Guimard with cartouche and title stamped in gold, signed lower right *HG* and lower left *V. Lelong sc.*

Gift of John Goelet

Le Castel Béranger was the architect Guimard's first building project (*habitation moderne*) in the Art Nouveau style, and considered his masterpiece, a block of luxury flats built between 1894 and 1898 near the Gare de Passy in Paris. Every element of the exterior and interior design and furnishing was from the drawing board of Guimard, forming a homogeneous and ornamental unit. The intricate asymmetry of the smooth and flowing lines of the wave-like title-page cartouche springs decisively from the Japanese woodcut.

Ref: Schmutzler, *Art Nouveau*, p. 117; Madsen, *Art Nouveau*, p. 112-115; Amaya, *Art Nouveau*, p. 119-121; Graham, *Hector Guimard*, p. 5, 28-29, cat. no. 57 ill.

70

Homer, *Navsikaa*
Leconte de Lisle, translator
Gaston de Latenay, illustrator
Paris, L'Edition d'Art, H. Piazza & Cie., 1899

Pictorial title-page, half-title, double-page frontispiece and justification and contents pages by
Gaston de Latenay, engraved in color, signed variously in the plates *GL 97* and *GL 98;* a total of 53
full-page decorative compositions by Latenay with
text borders, ornamental letters, fleurons and culs-
de-lampe. Printed by Imprimerie D. Dumoulin et
Cie.; new type "Louis XV" cast by the Fonderie
Turlot (Henri Chaix, succ.). Special watermarked
vélin paper fabricated by Les Papeteries d'Arches.

12¾ x 10¾ in. Gray-blue wrappers, upper and lower
covers engraved with foliate design by Latenay,
printed in pale sage-green and beige, signed with
monogram *GL98*; cream pebbled portfolio, title in
gold with blind stamp of L'Edition D'Art.
No. 198 of 375 numbered copies on *vélin*. Edition of
400 copies (25 on *Rives impériale* with extra suite
on china, 375 regular on *vélin*).

Purchased from the Caroline Miller Parker Fund

This story is an episode from the Odyssey. Leconte
de Lisle, the translator, was the leader of the Parnassian poets. Many of his writings were inspired
by Greek civilization, characterized by formal perfection and visual rather than emotive beauty. The
immobility and static archaeological style of the
poetry are matched by the pale, cool, lyrical coloring and formalized linear style of the illustrations
—landscapes with classical figures rhythmically
disposed.

Ref: Carteret, vol. 4, p. 235; Hofstätter, *Jugendstil Druckkunst,* p. 52-53 ill.

71

Charles Nodier, *Histoire du Chien de Brisquet*
Théophile Alexandre Steinlen, illustrator
Paris, Edouard Pelletan, 1900

Pictorial wrappers with wood-engraving designed

by Steinlen titled in blue, red and pale green, 4 full-
page wood-engravings in color and 19 black and
white vignettes designed by Steinlen, signed in the
blocks by the artist and the engravers, Deloche, E.
Froment, Ernest and Frédéric Florian, respectively. Printed by Lahure.

11½ x 9 in. No. 84 (copy for Henri Goldstein) of
127 copies on *grand vélin à cuve* with signed pro-
gressive proofs of the cover on japan, and 56 proofs
(4 unpublished), some signed by the engravers, on
japan, china and other papers.
Edition of 127 copies (1 on Whatman with original
drawing and double suite of proofs, 1 on Whatman
with original drawing for half-title and double
suite, 25 *grand vélin* with original drawing and
double suite; 100 regular on *grand vélin*).

Purchased from the Caroline Miller Parker Fund

This edition is dedicated to Jeanne (Pelletan), the
daughter of the publisher, to whom Anatole France
addressed his introduction, and was issued on the
occasion of the Exposition Universelle of 1900.
Conceived by the publisher to pull French book
production away from the dominance of the illustrator, this book is handsome in its apt balance
between the semiclassical typography and the illustrations; the cover deftly defines the Art
Nouveau style of Steinlen.

Ref: Lewis, *The Twentieth Century Book,* p. 37, 39-41.

72

Pierre Louÿs, *Byblis*
Henri Caruchet, illustrator
Paris, Librairie des Amateurs, A. Ferroud, 1901

Decorated title-page and colored frontispiece and
44 border designs hand-colored by Caruchet,
several signed *HC.* Printed by Philippe Renouard.

11¼ x 8 in. Dark olive-green morocco bound by
René Kieffer, inlaid upper and lower covers with
pale olive and ochre morocco design of vine leaves
and stylized water plant leaves, tooled and blind-
stamped; spine inlaid with leaves; doublures inlaid with celadon morocco panel with repeat
pattern of stylized blossom alternating in white

72. Henri Caruchet. Drawing for title-page of *Byblis*. 1901

and dark olive, tooled in gold; green brocade guards, edges gilt.

Unique copy, extra-illustrated, printed on Whatman Turkey Mill paper, with additional watercolor frontispiece signed *Henri Caruchet* and 46 preparatory drawings in color by the artist, signed with initials *HC,* with extra suite of black outlines printed on china paper. Edition of 300 copies (100 on japan or *grand vélin* with extra suite; 200 on Arches).

Lent by Raphael Esmerian.

Pierre Louÿs, associated with the Symbolists, was well-known for his *Chansons de Bilitis,* 1894, prose poem *d'amour antique,* posing as a translation from Greek of a poetess contemporary with Sappho. This earlier story is also a neo-classic pastoral in which the nymph Byblis succumbs to the love of a cruel hind and is led through the forest to her melancholy destruction. These stories with their mixture of the sensual and the erudite inevitably attracted the bibliophile and the deluxe binder. Henri Caruchet, with his soft harmonious line and mauve and pastel coloring, has clothed this idyll with floral border motifs in a graceful, dream-like setting.

Ref: Mahé, *Bibliographie,* vol. 2, p. 722; Carteret, vol. 5, p. 251; Talvert et Place, *Bibliographie,* vol. 12, p. 328.

73
George Auriol, *Le Premier Livre des Cachets, Marques et Monogrammes*
George Auriol, designer and illustrator
Paris, Librairie Centrale des Beaux-Arts, 1901

Title-page with lithographic vignette printed in green, title in red and green; pictorial frontispiece in red and green, and numerous marks, ornaments and vignettes throughout in red and green, each leaf with both type and ornament printed from one lithographic stone. Printed by Gustave de Malherbe.

7¾ x 5³⁄₁₆ in. Pink wrappers repeating title vignette by Auriol, lettered in red and black. One of regular edition on laid paper, in addition to which there were 30 numbered copies printed on *japon mat à la forme* decorated with an original fleuron.

Bequest of W. B. Osgood Field

George Auriol was highly gifted in book ornamentation in all its branches. He was responsible for several book covers, programmes, music covers and head- and tailpieces, both logical and fanciful in design. His reputation rests largely on his brushstroke typeface which, along with Grasset's type, was widely used in Art Nouveau printing. The rhythmic freedom and swelling lines were adapted to a breadth of expression. These marques and monograms, extremely japonesque, reveal Auriol at his inventive best. A second and third *Livre de Cachets* appeared in 1909 and 1924, respectively.

Ref: New York, The Museum of Modern Art, *Art Nouveau,* p. 39-40; Garvey, "Art Nouveau and the French Book of the Eighteen-Nineties," p. 387-388 ill.; "Studio Talk," 1901, p. 69 ill.

74
Hans Christian Andersen, *Histoires et Aventures*
Alexandre Lunois, illustrator
Paris, Chez l'Artiste, 1909

Title-page with water lily vignette by Alexandre Lunois printed in green and lettered in black and red; with 52 etchings (11 full-page) by Lunois printed in brown, and 80 color wood-engravings designed by Lunois; the wood-engravings cut by Suzanne Lepère and printed in color by E. Féquet.

10⅝ x 7 in. Cream wrappers encased in blue-gray cardboard portfolio. No. 107 of 125 numbered copies on *cuve d'Arches* paper with the watermark of the author and the monogram of Lunois. Edition of 146 copies (1 on japan with original water colors;

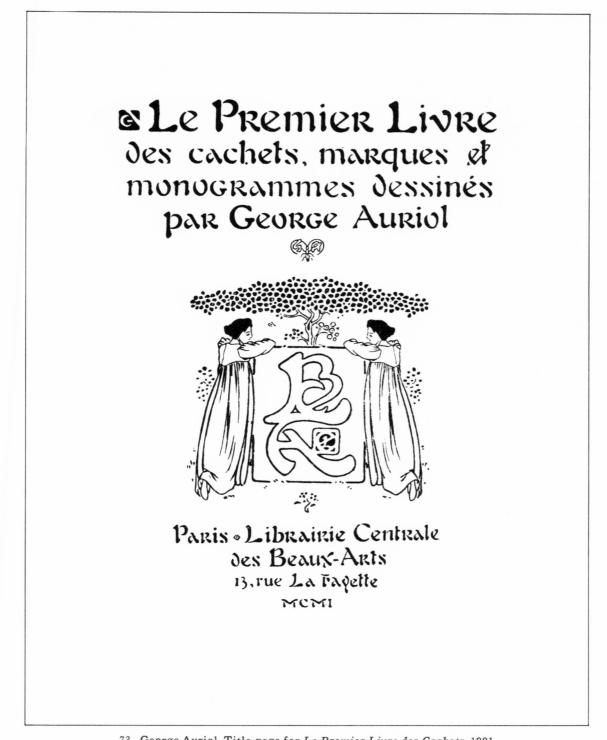

Le Premier Livre
des cachets, marques et
monogrammes dessinés
par George Auriol

Paris • Librairie Centrale
des Beaux-Arts
13, rue La Fayette
MCMI

73. George Auriol. Title-page for *Le Premier Livre des Cachets.* 1901

20 on japan with extra states of etchings and suite of wood-engravings; 125 on Arches; 10 suites of etchings and wood-engravings on china).

Gift of Peter A. Wick

Here is an example of an artist exercising full control over the design and layout of a book. Designed *à la japonais*, the etchings and color wood-engravings – including title, head- and tailpieces, initials and vignettes–further animate the lively text, which is also partly printed in red, brown and maroon.

Ref: Carteret, vol. 4, p. 44; Mahé, vol. 1, p. 39.

75
Edmond Rostand, *Chantecler*
René Lalique, designer of binding
Paris, Librairie Charpentier et Fasquelle, 1910

Half-title with facsimile of drawing of crowing rooster, hand-colored by the author. Otherwise unillustrated. Printed by Philippe Renouard.

$9\frac{1}{2}$ x $6\frac{1}{2}$ in. Brown limp suede with design of crowing rooster stamped in relief (the open beak forming the *C* for the title *Chantecler*), signed lower left *R. Lalique*. No. 375 of 1000 numbered copies on *papier impérial du Japon*.

Purchased from the William S. Spaulding Fund

Chantecler, an allegorical drama, is a later work of Rostand, thought by some critics to contain his best writing. René Lalique was a master craftsman and designer in the plastic arts, known particularly for his glass, crystal and jewelry in moulded relief design. His book covers are few and little known, and appropriately for *Chantecler* he exhibits his vivid mastery of animal attributes. Gustave Geffroy, describing a piece of jewelry, wrote: "He [Lalique] constructed a rooster head with the wide open beak about to swallow a diamond, more imprudent than La Fontaine's cock confronted with a delicate pearl, but this fellow is a *grand seigneur,* his crest and wattles encrusted with precious stones supplying thirty-six carats for nourishment, should it remain in his gullet."

Ref: Geffroy, *René Lalique*, p. 42; Schmutzler, *Art Nouveau,* p. 152.

BELGIUM
and HOLLAND
ITALY

Les lignes de très spéciale souplesse

A line is a force, filled with the energy
of him who drew it.

Henry van de Velde

76

Maurice Maeterlinck, *La Princesse Maleine*
George Minne, designer of binding
Ghent, chez van Melle, 1889

Unillustrated. Printed by Louis van Melle.

First copy: 7¼ x 5¼ in. Original parchment wrappers, upper cover with small woodcut of female head enveloped in her hair by George Minne, title printed in red. Red levant morocco, bound by Gruel, with purple silk doublures, edges gilt. Inscribed on flyleaf: *En toute sympathie / M. Maeterlinck.* One of 25 copies on *vélin teinté.* Edition of 30 copies (5 on van Gelder, 25 on *vélin*).

Purchased from the bequest of Amy Lowell

Second copy: 7⅜ x 5⅜ in. Parchment wrappers like first copy. One of 150 copies on *vélin teinté.*

Purchased from the bequest of Amy Lowell

This little volume is one of a uniform series printed by van Melle, of which *Serres Chaudes* (No. 77) is another. *La Princesse Maleine,* a drama in five acts, was, according to the publisher's notice,

written for a puppet theatre. Pierre Louÿs comments in his journal: *"La Princesse Maleine* is a strange and marvelous legend. It has the transparencies of nocturnal water, the shadows of a deep forest, dim and uniform hues which foretell the rumble of distant thunder. I would have liked to read it all, left alone in a heavily draped room without the shadow of another human, nor the echo of a sound. Not at night, however, because of the light, but in a nondescript dawn, grayer than daybreak, drabber than dusk, in a subdued and distant light dispelling a mysterious atmosphere. The voice in which I spoke to myself as I read very low remained slow and monotonous, without intending to drone, but as if weary and dying from inexhaustible sadness. The least inflection would have wounded me as a cruel dissonance."

Ref: Louÿs, *Journal Intime,* p. 355-56, 360.

77

Maurice Maeterlinck, *Serres Chaudes*
George Minne, illustrator
Paris, Léon Vanier, 1889

Frontispiece reproduced after drawing by George Minne and 6 woodcut vignettes by Minne. Printed by Louis van Melle, Ghent.

7¾ x 5⅝ in. Half aubergine morocco, white parchment sides, top edges silver-gilt. Original parchment wrappers bound in, with woodcut by Minne, lettered in red. No. 11 of 155 numbered copies on van Gelder paper. This copy with dedication on flyleaf: *à Léon Vanier / au noble éditeur des poètes / en toute sympathie / Maurice Maeterlinck.*

Purchased from the Caroline Miller Parker Fund

It would seem likely that several of these cuts by Minne exerted an influence on Maillol in his illustrations for Virgil's *Eclogues,* begun twenty-one years later. These poems by Maeterlinck were to influence Guillaume Apollinaire, by the latter's acknowledgement.

Ref: Brussels-Otterlo, *Le Groupe des XX et son Temps,* no. 188; Schmutzler, *Art Nouveau,* p. 140 ill.

78

Jules Destrée, *Les Chimères*
Marie Danse, Henry de Groux and *Odilon Redon,* illustrators
Brussels, Imprimerie Veuve Monnom, 1889

Frontispiece, *La Chimère*, lithograph on china paper by Odilon Redon; 2 full-page plates, one *La Gouge*, etching by Marie Danse (Mme. Jules Destrée-Danse), another, *La Forêt des Suicides*, drawing by Henry de Groux reproduced in lithography, dated and signed in the stone with monogram *1889 HD*. Printed by Bouwens, Brussels.

10½ x 8½ in. Cream wrappers, upper cover, design of seated gargoyle silhouetted against evening sky with crescent moon, author, title and date; lower cover, small bust of gargoyle, both etched by Marie Danse. No. 84 of 100 copies on fine laid paper. This copy sent by author to M. W. Ritter, Vienna.

Gift of Landon T. Clay

The visions, literary and visual, caught within these pages relate to the predecessors of this form of phantasmagoria: Rodolphe Bresdin, Charles Meryon, and above all Baudelaire. Destrée wrote a catalogue of Redon's lithographs in 1891.

Ref: Mellerio, *Odilon Redon*, no. 105; Brussels-Otterlo, *Le Groupe des XX et son Temps*, p. 19, 64, 131, no. 183.

79
Iwan Gilkin, *Ténèbres*
Odilon Redon, illustrator
Brussels, chez l'éditeur Edmond Deman, 1892.

Frontispiece lithograph on china paper by Odilon Redon; title-page with printer's device signed

with initials *FK* (Fernand Khnopff) and variant of same repeated as colophon. Printed by Alexandre Berqueman.

10¼ x 7¼ in. Half red morocco bound by René Kieffer, spine blind-tooled, top edges gilt. Original wrappers bound in, green-blue and black marbled with peacock feather design, title and printer's device stamped in gold. No. 73 of 150 numbered copies on van Gelder paper. Edition of 150 copies (10 on japan, 140 on van Gelder).

Gift of Mr. and Mrs. Arthur Vershbow

Gilkin, a Belgian poet, admired Redon, and the artist influenced the poet's imagery. *Ténèbres* was intended as a part of a trilogy, which included *La Damnation de l'Artiste*, and a third, *Satan*, unpublished. The winged figure holding a cauldron, lithographed by Redon in rich black on white, is a wonderful foil for the exotic lapidary cover.

Ref: Mellerio, *Odilon Redon*, no. 121; Boston Museum-Harvard College Library, *The Artist and the Book*, p. 172, no. 255.

80
Max Elskamp, *Dominical*
Henry van de Velde, designer
Antwerp, J. E. Buschmann, 1892

Unillustrated. Printer's device engraved on verso of final leaf. Printed by J. E. Buschmann.

8¾ x 5⁷⁄₁₆ in. Gray wrappers, upper cover with abstract bandeau designed by van de Velde printed in black in rectangular frame, title upper left; lower cover with small black device by van de Velde printed off center. No. 17 of 97 numbered copies on holland. Edition of 100 copies (3 on japan, 97 on holland). Inscribed on flyleaf: *à Iwan Gilkin: / en littéraire confraternité / respectueusement / Max Elskamp*.

Gift of Philip Hofer

Henry van de Velde was the Belgian apostle of Art Nouveau in architecture, decoration, and industrial art. Some of his cover designs are the finest of the period. The title-page of *Dominical* is one of the first deliberately asymmetrical typographical layouts in the history of book design. The composition on the cover, an expressionistic wave pattern of ebbing tide on a beach with rays of the setting sun on the horizon, is perhaps the earliest non-figurative abstract design in book illustration. It was followed in 1893 by similar striking abstractions for the periodical *Van Nu en Straks*. J. E. Buschmann was a poet and one of the foremost Belgian writers, as well as publisher and printer.

Ref: Day, *Book Typography*, p. 25-26, pl. 8; Hofstätter, *Jugendstil Druckkunst*, p. 137-138 ill.; Madsen, *Art Nouveau*, p. 99 ill.; Brussels-Otterlo, *Le Groupe des XX et son Temps*, no. 185.

81

Max Elskamp, *Salutations, dont d'angeliques*
Henry van de Velde, designer
Brussels, Paul Lacomblez, 1893

Unillustrated. Printed by J. E. Buschmann, Antwerp.

9 x 6¾ in. White paper wrappers, upper cover with enframed abstract design and title by van de Velde, printed in blue; lower cover with lily design printed in blue. Half tan cloth and blue paper over boards, title stamped in gold. No. 175 of 200 numbered copies on van Gelder. Edition of 203 copies (3 on japan, 200 on van Gelder).

Gift of Richard W. Hale

Van de Velde revered the art and teachings of William Morris, yet in his own book production radically split from his English mentor, especially in his attitude towards ornament. This cover with its bold and rhythmical curvilinear design and the unconventional lettering, which have a movement of their own, are in perfect unity but are entirely abstract. In 1895 *Salutations* became part of *Triptyque de louange à la vie, selon l'amour, l'espérance et la foie*, which also included *Dominical* (No. 80) and *En symbole vers l'Apostolat*.

Ref: Day, *Book Typography*, p. 25; Brussels-Otterlo, *Le Groupe des XX et son Temps*, no. 184.

82

Max Elskamp, *Six Chansons de Pauvre Homme pour célébrer la Semaine de Flandre*
Max Elskamp, designer
Brussels, Imprimé chez Henry van de Velde pour P. Lecomblez, 1895

Title-page with horizontal frieze and oval ornament by Elskamp, printed in yellow-ochre; total of 35 ornaments as chapter headings, tailpieces and ornaments in text, printed in yellow-ochre. Printed on a hand press.

6⅞ x 5 in. Brown paper boards repeating ornaments of title-page by Elskamp, printed in yellow-ochre. No. 130 of 150 numbered copies on china. Edition of 154 copies (4 deluxe on *chine-fort*, 150 regular on china).

Purchased from The Caroline Miller Parker Fund

The poems and ornaments of this little book are by van de Velde's friend Max Elskamp. The choice of Caslon type and layout of the book was by van de Velde himself. Remy de Gourmont paid the following tribute in *Le Livre des Masques*: "I like the poets who had the taste for external beauty and who dressed with real grace their inspirational graces, but none had the artistic purity comparable to *Six chansons de pauvre homme.* . . ."

Ref: Day, *Book Typography*, p. 25, pl. 9.

83

Pol de Mont, *Iris*
Dedicated to Dr. Max Rooses
Antwerp, J. E. Buschmann, 1894

Decorated title-page with woodcut border of iris printed in pale green, etched frontispiece portrait of author by Ph. Zilcken, signed in the plate; 9 illustrations reproducing drawings by Hendricus Jansen, Fernand Khnopff, Karel Mertens, G. Rochegrosse and Fritz von Uhde. Each page of text with floral woodcut borders printed in green or yellow-ochre; chapter headings and floral initials printed in black.

Max Elskamp.

Salutations,

dont d'angéliques

Paul LACOMBLEZ, éditeur.

81. Henry van de Velde. Cover for *Salutations*. 1893

10⅞ x 6⅞ in. Buff imitation vellum with woodcut iris design printed in black, signed lower right *PB*. One of 250 numbered copies printed on van Gelder.

Purchased from the Caroline Miller Parker Fund

This book comprises the author's collected poems in Dutch, one series inspired by selected verse of Verlaine on impressions from nature. It is handsomely and freshly printed with narrow columns of text hugging the inside of the page so as to give full expression to the woodcut borders, which seem to spring verdantly from a fertile soil.

Ref: Hague, Museum Meermanno-Westreenianum, *Het Nederlandse Boek*, no. 278.

84

Emile Verhaeren, *Les Villes Tentaculaires*
Théo van Rysselberghe, designer of covers
Dedicated to Henri de Regnier
Brussels, chez l'éditeur Edmond Deman, 1895

Ornaments by Théo van Rysselberghe.
Printed by Alexandre Berqueman.

9 x 6¼ in. Gray paper wrappers with enframed design of octopus by van Rysselberghe printed in dark gray, title printed in crimson; lower cover with tiger lily; ornamented half-title. Gray boards repeating design of wrappers. No. 121 on *vélin teinté*. Edition of 595 copies (5 on imperial japan, 15 on holland, 575 on *vélin*). This copy inscribed on flyleaf: *à Michael Sadler / son ami / Emil Verhaeren*. Bookplate of Betty and Michael Sadler.

Purchased from the bequest of Amy Lowell

In describing the book illustration of Félicien Rops, Fernand Baudin remarks: "Rops made his letters an integral part of the composition, to the extent that you cannot separate the two. . . ." This applies to van Rysselberghe's design in which the octopus not only coils about the frame but almost creates the letters themselves. Equally decorative are the coiled salamander device and the owl, Art Nouveau motifs used with power yet restraint as decoration, rather than illustration. *Les Villes Tentaculaires* was the second in a series, beginning with *Les Campagnes Hallucinées,* ending with *Les Aubes* (No. 87).

Ref: Day, *Book Typography*, p. 21; Uzanne, *L'Art dans la Décoration des Livres*, p. 92 ill.; Culot, *Bibliographie de Verhaeren*, p. 17; Ghent, Musée des Beaux Arts, *Théo van Rysselberghe*, no. 290.

85

Emile Verhaeren, *Almanach, cahier de vers*
Théo van Rysselberghe, illustrator
Brussels, Dietrich & Co., 1895

Title-page vignette, 4 full-page illustrations, 12 head- and tailpieces, vignettes and initials by Théo van Rysselberghe. Printed by Mme. Veuve Monnom in blue and black.

First copy: 8¼ x 8 in. Pale gray wrappers, upper cover with enframing design of morning glories by van Rysselberghe printed in blue. One of 250 copies printed in Delft blue on Ingres paper. Edition of 1050 copies (50 on japan, signed and numbered by the authors, 250 printed in mauve, 250 in orange, 250 in blue, 250 in green). Bookplate of Michael Sadler.

Purchased from the bequest of Amy Lowell

Second copy: 8¼ x 7⅞ in. Gray boards. This copy one of 250 printed in green on Ingres paper. Inscribed inside wrapper: *à Michael Sadler / pour que les douze mois de chaque / année lui soient bienveillants / Emile Verhaeren*. Bookplate of Michael Sadler.

Purchased from the bequest of Amy Lowell

The cover design by van Rysselberghe of morning

85. Théo van Rysselberghe. Cover for *Almanach*. 1895

glories, twined about the frame and spreading in luxuriant growth across the cover in unison with the lettering, is a perfect balance of Art Nouveau decorative form and typography.

Ref: Schmutzler, *Art Nouveau*, p. 48 ill.; Uzanne, *L'Art dans la Décoration des Livres*, p. 92 ill.; Day, *Book Typography*, p. 253, pl. 11 ill.; Culot, *Bibliographie de Verhaeren*, p. 16; Ghent, Musée des Beaux Arts, *Théo van Rysselberghe*, no. 291.

86

Emile Verhaeren, *Les Heures Claires*
Théo van Rysselberghe, designer
Brussels, chez l'éditeur Edmond Deman, 1896

58 head- and tailpieces (12 different designs) by Théo van Rysselberghe and/or Juliette Wytsman. Printed by Alexandre Berqueman, with vignettes in orange.

8⅛ x 5½ in. Stippled light gray-green wrappers, upper cover with title in orange and design of three butterflies, lower cover with printer's device in orange signed with initials *FK* (Fernand Khnopff). Ordinary paper copy. There were also 5 copies on japan and 20 on holland. Inscribed in pen: *à Michael Sadler / Emile Verhaeren / & Martha Vehaeren*. Bookplate of Betty and Michael Sadler.

Purchased from the bequest of Amy Lowell

The ephemeral quality of the poetry is announced by the cover with its elusive butterflies fluttering about the brilliant orange of the title. The delicacy and spatter technique ("crachis") of this cover lithograph is evocative of the style of Toulouse-Lautrec. Although van Rysselberghe's name does not appear in the book, Paul Eeckhout's catalogue of the 1962 Ghent exhibition includes it among his many books designed for his friend Verhaeren. Culot's bibliography of Verhaeren, on the other hand, gives the head- and tailpieces to Juliette Wytsman.

Ref: Culot, *Bibliographie de Verhaeren*, p. 17; Ghent, Musée des Beaux Arts, *Théo van Rysselberghe*, no. 292.

87

Emile Verhaeren, *Les Aubes*
Théo van Rysselberghe, designer
Dedicated to Paul Signac
Brussels, chez l'éditeur Deman, 1898

One decorated headpiece by van Rysselberghe. Printed by Alexandre Berqueman.

9¼ x 6½ in. Gray wrappers, upper cover with enframed design by van Rysselberghe printed in olive-green and orange, lower cover with printer's device signed with initials *FK (Fernand Khnopff)*. Gray boards repeating design of wrappers. Ordinary paper copy. There were also 5 copies on imperial japan and 15 on holland. Inscribed on flyleaf: *à Michael Sadler / ce livre de paix, en temps de guerre / Emile Verhaeren, le 19 Sept. 14*. Bookplate of Betty and Michael Sadler.

Purchased from the bequest of Amy Lowell

An ornamental frame surrounds the sun rising behind the curve of the dark earth, crossed diagonally by a surging flame-like motif. The names of the title, author, and publisher are unobtrusively incorporated into the design, oriental in flavor and conception, but entirely northern in impact. Van Rysselberghe was responsible for bringing Neo-Impressionism to Belgium, yet had, at the same time, strong ties to Art Nouveau.

Ref: Culot, *Bibliographie de Verhaeren*, p. 18; Ghent, Musée des Beaux Arts, *Théo van Rysselberghe*, p. 76.

86. Théo van Rysselberghe. Cover for *Les Heures Claires*. 1896

88

Auguste, comte de Villiers de l'Isle-Adam, *Histoires Souveraines*
Théo van Rysselberghe, designer
Brussels, Edmond Deman, 1899

Decorated title-page, 40 floral chapter headings, tailpiece, and ornaments by Théo van Rysselberghe. Printed by Alexandre Berqueman, with ornaments in sage-green and gray.

First copy: $10\frac{1}{4}$ x $7\frac{3}{16}$ in. Green morocco signed with the binder's monogram *LJB,* upper and lower covers inlaid with border design after van Rysselberghe in pale green calf, top edges gilt, figured green end papers, cover guard. Original metallic green wrappers bound in, upper cover lettered in gold with repetition of title-page design, lower cover with printer's device in black signed with initials *FK* (Fernand Khnopff). No. 48 of 50 numbered copies on japan. Edition of 60 copies (10 on van Gelder, 50 on japan).

Gift of Peter A. Wick

Second copy: $10\frac{1}{2}$ x $7\frac{1}{8}$ in. Original metallic green wrappers like first copy. Half red morocco. One of 10 copies on van Gelder.

Purchased from Subscription Fund

This is one of the most ambitious books published by Edmond Deman, with its quarto format, layout and ornamentation by van Rysselberghe–certainly one of the most restrained and discreet books to fall under the name of Art Nouveau.

Ref: Day, *Book Typography,* p. 21-22, pl. 10; Ghent, Musée des Beaux Arts, *Théo van Rysselberghe,* no. 297.

89

Thomas Braun, *L'An*
Franz M. Melchers, illustrator
Brussels, E. Lyon-Claeson, 1897

Pictorial title-page with abstract wave design by Melchers printed in olive-green, title in lavender, with *remarque* of artist lower right; 16 full-page color woodblock prints by Melchers, signed with *remarque.*

$13\frac{5}{8}$ x $12\frac{5}{8}$ in. Gray wrappers with title stamped in small block and *remarques* of author and artist printed in black. No. 9 of 50 numbered copies on holland. Edition of 1070 copies (20 on *japon impériale,* 50 on holland, 1000 on *vélin*).

Gift of Philip Hofer

This large folio of Braun's poems on the changing seasons shows the marked influence of Japanese color woodblocks, while the wave-like vibrations in the pictorial title-page echo the current idiom of Munch and van Gogh.

Ref: Mont, "Frantz M. Melchers."

90

Henrietta van der Schalk, *Sonnetten en Verzen in Terzinen Geschreven*
R. N. Roland Holst, designer
Amsterdam, Scheltema en Holkema's Boekhandel, 1895

Title-page with ornament and lettering in woodcut by R. N. Roland Holst, printed in red and black, half-title with decorated initial and ornament in red and black, 7 chapter headings with decorated initial and ornament, lined in red throughout; numerous type ornaments. Printed by Joh. Enschedé en Zonen, Haarlem.

8⅝ x 7 in. Half linen, gray-blue boards, upper cover with title printed in black, repeating half-title. Printed on holland paper.

Gift of Peter A. Wick

The prime mover for much good book design in Holland was K. Groesbeck, director of both the publishing firm of Scheltema and Holkema and the art shop Van Wisselingh. He encouraged such designers as G. W. Dijsselhof and Theo Nieuwenhuis. In 1893 Dijsselhof had illustrated a Dutch edition of Walter Crane's *Claims of Decorative Art* with an extraordinary cover design based on a batik pattern. The *Sonnetten* were decorated by the author's fiancé, Richard Roland Holst, who later became Director of the Royal Academy of Art. G. W. Ovink describes this book: with "wormlike lombardics and the same gothic filigree mixed with fluent, lobed-plant ornaments and pithy, hard woodcut decorations; the whole anchored down with red lines in the page format." The distinction of these pages owes much to the famous Haarlem printers Enschedé en Zonen.

Ref: Day, *Book Typography,* p. 252.

91

Hélène Lapidoth-Swarth, *Diepe Wateren*
L. W. R. Wenckebach, designer of binding
Amsterdam, P. N. van Kampen & Zoon, 1897

Unillustrated.

6¾ x 4⅝ in. White linen boards, upper cover decorated in olive-green with design by Wenckebach of three water lilies and a fish swimming under water, signed with monogram lower right *WRW.* Copy stamped with collector's mark: *F. M. Goeyen.*

Gift of Peter A. Wick

Wenckebach illustrated another book by this author, *Octoberloover,* 1903

Ref: Hague, Museum Meermanno-Westreenianum, *Het Nederlandse Boek,* no. 44 ill.

92

Louis Couperus, *Psyche*
Jan Toorop, designer of binding
Amsterdam, L. J. Veen, 1898

Unillustrated.

8⅛ x 6 in. Beige linen boards, upper cover with design of Psyche riding the winged horse by Jan Toorop printed in blue; lower cover with floral and radial pattern.

Gift of Peter A. Wick

Others book covers designed by Toorop are Louise Ahn-de Jong, *Een boek van verbeelding,* 1893; Louis Couperus, *Babel,* 1899; Henri Borel, *Een droom,* 1899; van Nouhuys, *Egidius en de Vreedeling,* 1899 (No. 93); Netty Spanjaard, *Louise Geertsma Verheulen,* 1900.

Ref: Hague, Museum Meermanno-Westreenianum, *Het Nederlandse Boek,* no. 56.

93

W. G. van Nouhuys, *Egidius en de Vreedeling*
Jan Toorop, designer of cover
Haarlem, Erven F. Bohn, 1899

Frontispiece portrait reproduced after drawing by Jan Toorop and 2 full-page illustrations in reproduction.

11¼ x 8 in. Sand colored wrappers, upper cover with design by Toorop of kneeling maiden with curvilinear patterns printed in burnt sienna, signed at bottom *J. Toorop*; lower cover with border design. No. 29 of 200 numbered copies on holland.

Gift of Peter A. Wick

Toorop, who was born in Java, perpetuated the flaming, whirling, waving forms of Art Nouveau long after they were generally repudiated in Holland and elsewhere on the Continent. This particular cover design has warped even the lettering into almost illegible compressed shapes.

Ref: Hague, Museum Meermanno-Westreenianum, *Het Nederlandse Boek,* no. 80 ill.; Schmutzler, *Art Nouveau,* p. 148 ill.

94

Pieter Hendrik van Moerkerken, Jr., *Modron, een dramatisch spel*
Pieter Hendrik van Moerkerken, Jr., designer
Amsterdam, S. L. van Looy, 1903

Pictorial title-page with woodcut of two female figures beneath a stylized tree by P. H. van Moerkerken, printed in black with lettering and ornament. Printed by Gaarlandt en Tjabring.

7½ x 4⅞ in. Original gray wrappers repeating design of title-page with cut printed in yellow, lettering in red. Printed on van Gelder paper.

Gift of Peter A. Wick

The balanced simplicity and stylization of this little woodcut, at once archaic and modern in design, combine well with the uncial-like lettering.

Ref: Hague, Museum Meermanno-Westreenianum, *Het Nederlandse Boek,* no. 176 ill.

95

Anna van Gogh-Kaulbach, *Kleine Menschen*
Amsterdam, P. N. van Kampen & Zoon, 1907

Unillustrated.

8½ x 6⅜ in. Original olive-green cloth, decorated with sinuous design of stylized chrysanthemums and abstract yellow wreath, printed in rust and yellow, titled in gold. End papers with intricate interlacing in shades of olive-green. Designer unknown.

Gift of Peter A. Wick

This cover design was first used in 1901 for Henri Borel's *Van de engelen.*

Ref: Hague, Museum Meermanno-Westreenianum, *Het Nederlandse Boek,* no. 115.

96

L.E., *Silhouetten*
Amsterdam, Van Holkema & Warendorf, 1909

Unillustrated.

9 x 7 in. Original white cloth boards, decorated with peacock design of green, blue, yellow and

black framing title printed in gold. End papers of floral wreath design printed in tan on cream. Binding signed lower cover: *Elias van Bommel, Amsterdam.* Designer unknown.

The peacock, one of the common denominators of Art Nouveau decoration, is here applied to a book cover in a heavy manner, at a time when the style had passed its creative peak.

97

Gabriele d'Annunzio, *Francesca da Rimini*
Adolfo de Carolis, illustrator
Dedicated to Eleanora Duse
Milan, Fratelli Treves, 1902

Architectural title-page and ex-libris page, 2 borders, 5 full-page decorations, including colophon, vignettes, and initials by Adolfo de Carolis, printed in red and black.

First copy: 9¼ x 7¾ in. Original vellum with ties, upper cover gilt-stamped with device of wreath,

book, and sword with motto, "Noi leggevamo," spine gilt-stamped with title and interlaced borders.

Bequest of Amy Lowell

Second copy: 9¼ x 7¾ in. Original light brown linen with ties, gilt-stamped like first copy.

Gift of Mrs. Henry F. Bryan

In Italy, Art Nouveau was known as the *stile floreale* or *stile Liberty,* from the figured fabrics of Arthur Lasenby Liberty, which were as popular and influential in the Nineties as William Morris' textiles had been in the Eighties. The style was of late development in Italy, and the tradition too classical for much of the experimentation seen elsewhere. Adolfo de Carolis, who revived the art of the Italian woodcut, illustrated several books by d'Annunzio in the new idiom. Although his interest in the Quattrocento and in monumental figure style is apparent, the details of his small vignettes and initials contain many unclassical and modern style elements. One of the most striking is the serpentine Medusa head punningly dedicated "alla divina Eleanora Duse."

Ref: Hofstätter, *Jugendstil Druckkunst,* p. 203-205 ill.

GERMANY and AUSTRIA

Art is art, precisely because it is not nature.
Goethe

I am particularly interested in the square as such and in the use of black and white as dominant colors, because these clear elements have never appeared in earlier styles.
Josef Hoffmann

Der Zeit ihre Kunst,
Der Kunst ihre Freiheit.

Inscription on
J. M. Olbrich's
Secession Building,
Vienna

98

Pan

Otto Julius Bierbaum and Julius Meier-Graefe, editors

Berlin, 1895-1900, 5 volumes (separate numbers issued irregularly).

First volume with illustrations and decorations by several artists, including Charles Doudelet, Otto Eckmann, Fernand Khnopff, Max Klinger, Joseph Sattler, Félix Vallotton, E. R. Weiss. Printed by various printers for different media (the magazine included some original graphic work, as well as reproductions and line cuts).

14½ x 10⅝ in. Original wrappers, upper cover with head of Pan by Franz Stuck, signed *Franz Stuck*. This cover design appeared on all the issues, printed in different colors.

Given in memory of Archibald Cary Coolidge

Pan was the first significant German periodical of the Nineties devoted to contemporary art and literature. Although it included other European contributions, the emphasis was on the Germans, sometimes on late Romanticism. As the years advanced, the influence of the Jugendstil became more prominent, and the work of Otto Eckmann, who designed many of the ornamental vignettes, is especially striking.

Ref: Bremen, Kunsthalle, *Europäischer Jugendstil*, p. 62.

99

Die Insel,
Monatschrift mit Buchschmuck und Illustrationen
Otto Julius Bierbaum, Alfred Walter Heymel, and Rudolf Alexander Schröder, editors
Berlin, Schuster & Loeffler, 1899–1901; Leipzig, Insel-Verlag, 1902

First issue (October, 1899) includes prose and poetry by Bierbaum, Heymel, Schröder, Hugo von Hofmannsthal, Julius Meier-Graefe, Clemens Brentano, Detlev von Liliencron. Layout by Georges Lemmen. Illustrations by Lemmen, Thomas Theodor Heine, Wilhelm Laage. Printed by W. Drugulin, Leipzig.

9½ x 7½ in. (first and second years); 8½ x 5¾ in. (third year).
First year (Oct. 1899–Sept. 1900): Each quarter (3 issues) with new cover design, in different colors for each issue; printed wrappers with abstract floral designs, printed white labels with Insel-Verlag ship designed by Peter Behrens frequently used on upper covers.
Second year (Oct. 1900–Sept. 1901): Printed wrappers with over-all design of Insel-Verlag ship against stylized waves, each issue in different colors.
Third year (Oct. 1901–Sept. 1902): Smaller format. Upper covers with title in central panel, stylized foliate borders in mustard yellow (7 issues), later in red, blue, gold.

The Rilke collection of Richard von Mises.
Purchased from the bequest of Amy Lowell

99. Heinrich Vogeler. Page of *Die Insel*. March, 1900

The first issue of *Die Insel* is dated October, 1899, and it continued as a monthly until September, 1902. During the last year, with Birnbaum the only editor, the imprint is no longer Schuster and Loeffler, but Insel-Verlag, Leipzig. Like the Munich periodicals *Pan* (1895) and *Jugend* (1896), which gave its name to the Jugendstil in Germany, *Die Insel* was an influential journal, both intellectually and stylistically. It published not only German, but other European writers and artists. E. R. Weiss, Heinrich Vogeler and Marcus Behmer figure prominently in its pages, along with Félix Vallotton, William Nicholson, George Minne, Maurice Denis, and Laurence Housman. Meier-Graefe wrote an article on Loie Fuller, illustrated by Th. Th. Heine, but without the linear brilliance with which Toulouse-Lautrec and Will Bradley depicted her. The Belgian Georges Lemmen designed the layout of the first quarter of *Die Insel*, Heinrich Vogeler the second, and E. R. Weiss the third. Peter Behrens was the designer of the Insel device of a ship within an open circle, used as cover design, imprint, label, and watermark on various Insel-Verlag publications. *Die Insel* experimented with typography and with vignettes and ornaments in the new style, and from the same editors and artists came the Insel Books (Nos. 100-102), which set a high standard of design in twentieth-century German book production.

Ref: Loubier, *Die Neue Deutsche Buchkunst,* pl. 9-10 ill.; Schauer, *Deutsche Buchkunst,* vol. 1, p. 26-30, vol. 2, pl. 11 ill.; Bremen, Kunsthalle, *Europäischer Jugendstil,* p. 66, pl. 152-153 ill.

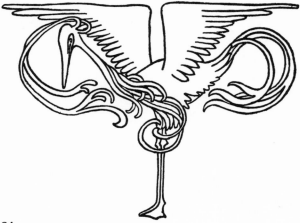

100

Otto Julius Bierbaum, *Gugeline, ein Buehnenspiel in fünf Aufzügen*
Alfred Walter Heymel, editor
Emil Rudolf Weiss, illustrator
Dedicated to Ludwig Thuille
Berlin, Schuster & Loeffler, "Insel" Buch, 1899

12 full-page decorations and vignettes by E. R. Weiss, several signed with initials *ERW*. Printed by W. B. Drugulin, Leipzig.

First copy: 7½ x 5⅜ in. Original buff boards, upper cover printed with title within decorative green and yellow tree with birds, lower printed with design of stylized green and yellow tree, ribbon, and bird by Weiss, signed with initials *ERW*, spine with yellow-green lettering and floral design; yellow edges, blue and green curvilinear leaf design end papers. One of 25 regular copies. Edition of 30 copies (25 regular, 5 hand-colored by the artist).

Purchased from Subscription Fund

Second copy: 7½ x 5⅜ in. Original boards like first copy.

Lent by the Busch-Reisinger Museum

Gugeline, published in May, 1899, was the first book to bear the imprint of the "Insel," the name of the periodical (No. 99) published from October, 1899 to 1902 under the guidance of Bierbaum, A. W. Heymel, and R. A. Schröder. Although the work of E. R. Weiss in *Gugeline* is still somewhat traditional, based on folk art sources, the curvilinear, spiraling line of his abstract designs and his end papers partake of the Jugendstil.

Ref: Schauer, *Deutsche Buchkunst,* vol. 1, p. 28, vol. 2, pl. 5 ill.; Hofstätter, *Jugendstil Druckkunst,* p. 141; Schmutzler, *Art Nouveau,* p. 20, 280 ill.

101

Alfred Walter Heymel, *Die Fischer und Andere Gedichte*
Emil Rudolf Weiss, illustrator
Dedicated to Otto Julius Bierbaum
Leipzig, Insel-Verlag, 1899

Decorated title-page, dedication page, 8 full-page decorations, vignettes and ornaments by E. R. Weiss. Printed by W. Drugulin on paper watermarked with Insel-Verlag ship.

6¾ x 4½ in. Original half vellum, decorated boards and end papers printed in curvilinear design of light and dark reddish-brown by Weiss. Printed white label with Insel-Verlag ship on upper cover. One of regular copies on laid paper with watermark of Insel-Verlag ship. In addition, 20 numbered copies were printed on imperial japan and bound in full vellum.

Purchased from the Morris Gray Fund

Following Bierbaum's *Gugeline* (No. 100), which appeared in May, 1899, Heymel's *Die Fischer* was published in October and is another of the early books with the imprint of the Insel-Verlag. It bears on the flyleaf, the label and the watermark the Insel device of a ship within an open circle designed by Peter Behrens, which appeared the same month in the first issue of the periodical *Die Insel* (No. 99). In this book Weiss is no longer dependent on the traditional sources of *Gugeline*. His designs are based on plant forms, highly abstracted and stylized into flat, serpentine shapes incorporating the lettering that Weiss later developed into several alphabets and type founts.

Ref: Schauer, *Deutsche Buchkunst*, vol. 1, p. 27-28, vol. 2, pl. 5 ill.; Hofstätter, *Jugendstil Druckkunst*, p. 141; Bremen, Kunsthalle, *Europäischer Jugendstil*, no. 122, pl. 65 ill.

102

Rainer Maria Rilke, *Vom Lieben Gott und Anderes, An Grosse für Kinder*
Emil Rudolf Weiss, illustrator
Berlin and Leipzig, Schuster & Loeffler, Insel-Verlag, 1900

Decorated title-page, 25 head- and tailpieces, ornaments, and initials by E. R. Weiss, several signed with initials *ERW*. Printed by W. Drugulin, Leipzig.

8¼ x 5½ in. Half gray cloth, gray marbled board sides and end papers, black morocco label on spine.

The Rilke collection of Richard von Mises.
Purchased from the bequest of Amy Lowell

Like *Gugeline* (No. 100) of the previous year, E. R. Weiss' illustrations for the Rilke of 1900 are reminiscent of folk art, but several of his designs break away from this tradition. Using free and dynamic curves, he evolved an abstract foliate ornament of strong linear outline, sometimes fusing floral and figured elements. He also experimented with ornamental calligraphic shapes to break up the monotony of the printed black-letter line. None of the books included here with work by Weiss was illustrated in a literal fashion. They were, rather, decorated, and they are variously described in their contents as "mit Buchschmuck von E. R. Weiss" or "Geschmückt von E. R. Weiss." In 1901 these Rilke sheets were reissued with a new title-page.

Ref: Schmutzler, *Art Nouveau*, p. 191 ill.; Hofstätter, *Jugendstil Druckkunst*, p. 141; Hünich, *Rilke-Bibliographie*, p. 36; Ritzer, *Rilke Bibliographie*, p. 33, E25.

103

Otto Julius Bierbaum, *Der Bunte Vogel, ein Kalenderbuch*
Félix Vallotton and *Emil Rudolf Weiss,* illustrators (1897); *Peter Behrens,* illustrator (1899)
Berlin and Leipzig, Schuster & Loeffler, 1897 and 1899. 2 numbers.

Der Bunte Vogel von 1897: Numerous vignettes and ornaments by Félix Vallotton and E. R. Weiss, including several signed with initials *FV, ERW,* and *W*.
Printed by W. Drugulin, Leipzig.
Der Bunte Vogel von 1899: Numerous vignettes and ornaments by Peter Behrens. Printed by Otto von Holten, Berlin.

Der Bunte Vogel von 1897: 8½ x 7 in. Original buff wrappers, upper cover printed with title and multicolor bird and grass by Vallotton, signed with initials *FV,* lower cover with two geese in flight, spine with ostrich. One of 15 copies on German handmade paper of special edition of 30 copies (5 on imperial japan, 10 on holland, 15 on German handmade paper).

Der Bunte Vogel von 1899: 8½ x 7 in. Original buff wrappers, upper cover with title within stylized green and blue peacock design by Behrens, signed with initial *B*, lower cover with three roses in yellow and blue, spine with peacock. One of 1300 regular copies. Edition of 1330 copies (1300 regular, 15 on German handmade paper, 10 on holland, 5 on imperial japan).

Gift of Peter A. Wick

Der Bunte Vogel issued from the same milieu as *Die Insel* (No. 99) and shares some of the same characteristics. Smaller and more traditional in format, these little almanachs contain many elements of the Jugendstil, especially in the issue designed by Peter Behrens.

Ref: Schauer, *Deutsche Buchkunst*, vol. 1, p. 27, 43, vol. 2, pl. 6 ill.; Hofstätter, *Jugendstil Druckkunst*, p. 125, 130 ill.; New York, The Museum of Modern Art, *Art Nouveau*, p. 36 ill.

104

Adolf Wilbrandt, *Der Sänger*
Otto Eckmann, designer of binding
Stuttgart, J. G. Cotta, 1899

Unillustrated. Printed by the Union Deutsche Verlagsgesellschaft.

7¼ x 4¾ in. Original cream cloth, upper cover and spine gilt- and black-stamped with title and stylized floral design by Otto Eckmann, signed with monogram *OE*.

Purchased from the George Silsbee and Ellen Seaver Hale Fund

Otto Eckmann, one of the most influential German graphic designers and a leader of the German floral style, produced several Jugendstil type faces, and his work appears in many pages of *Pan* and *Jugend*. He also designed bindings, and the sharp, dark sil-

houetted floral style of this one suggests the forms of metalwork, another craft for which he designed.

Ref: New York, The Museum of Modern Art, *Art Nouveau*, p. 168; Schauer, *Deutsche Buchkunst*, vol. 1, p. 36-39; Hofstätter, *Jugendstil Druckkunst*, p. 132-135.

105

Heinrich Vogeler, *Dir, Gedichte*
Heinrich Vogeler, illustrator
Berlin, Schuster & Loeffler, Insel-Verlag, 1899

Decorated title-page, half-title, and 30 vignettes by Heinrich Vogeler, several designed as frames for lettered verses. Printed by W. Drugulin, Leipzig, on paper watermarked with Insel-Verlag ship.

9½ x 7 in. Original half vellum, gray boards printed with yellow stripes and design of flower in yellow and green, upper cover with printed white label with Insel-Verlag ship, green end papers with floral design in green and yellow.
One of regular copies. In addition to the regular copies, 40 numbered copies were printed on van Gelder paper of which 6 were hand-colored by the artist and bound in vellum.

Purchased from the bequest of Hugo Reisinger

Heinrich Vogeler is sometimes called Vogeler-Worpswede from the location of his studio-estate near Bremen, where he founded the Worpsweder Werkstätten für Landhausmöbel in 1908 and, like so many of his German contemporaries, worked in various fields of art and design. He did layouts and illustration for *Die Insel* (No. 99), as well as books for the young publishing house. *Dir* presents him as poet and artist, with the verses written out in Roman letters rather than set in type. Vogeler's vignettes are composed of figures and floral forms, and the most individual pages are those on which the text is framed by the attenuated, interwoven floral composition.

Ref: Loubier, *Die Neue Deutsche Buchkunst*, pl. 23 ill.; Schauer, *Deutsche Buchkunst*, vol. 1, p. 47, vol. 2, pl. 12 ill.; Hofstätter, *Jugendstil Druckkunst*, p. 157-158; Bremen, Kunsthalle, *Europäischer Jugendstil*, no. 219, pl. 164 ill.

104. Otto Eckmann. Binding for *Der Sänger*. 1899

106

Hugo von Hofmannsthal, *Der Kaiser und Die Hexe*
Heinrich Vogeler, illustrator
Berlin, Schuster & Loeffler, Insel-Verlag, 1900

Decorated title-page, frontispiece, and initials by Heinrich Vogeler. Printed by Otto von Holten in color and gold on paper watermarked with Insel-Verlag ship.

8⅞ x 5½ in. Original full vellum, title gilt-stamped on spine, gilt-stamped foliate dentelles, end papers with stylized foliate design in red, green, and gold. No. 115 of 200 copies.

Gift of Gilbert H. Montague

The title-page and facing frontispiece of *Der Kaiser und die Hexe* are similar in conception to Vogeler's colophon page for issue no. 6 (March, 1900) of *Die Insel* (No. 99). These designs have medieval sources, with as much emphasis placed on the wide decorative borders as on the inner illustrations, which are composed with the same sweeping linear scheme.

Ref: Schauer, *Deutsche Buchkunst,* vol. 1, p. 47, vol. 2, pl. 11 ill.; Hofstätter, *Jugendstil Druckkunst,* p. 157-158, pl. 159 ill.; Bremen, *Europäischer Jugendstil,* no. 220; The Houghton Library, *Vienna 1888-1938,* no. 43 ill.

107

Hugo von Hofmannsthal, *Das Gerettete Venedig,*
Trauerspiel in fünf Aufzügen
Josef Hoffmann, designer of binding
Berlin, S. Fischer Verlag, 1905

Unillustrated. Printed by W. Drugulin, Leipzig.

6⅝ x 4½ in. Full orange morocco, design of gilt triangles with stylized plant on both covers, gilt title and plant on spine by Josef Hoffmann for the Wiener Werkstätte; edges gilt, multi-color marbled end papers. Inside front cover gilt-stamped with *Wiener Werkstätte* and 3 monograms: *JH* (Josef Hoffmann), *CB* (Carl Beitel) and *LW* (Ludwig Willner), binders. Presentation copy with inscription from the author to Count Harry Kessler.

An example of Hoffmann's geometric Wiener Werkstätte style leading away from the Jugendstil into twentieth-century geometric forms is seen in this binding, executed with superb craftsmanship by Beitel and Willner. The Wiener Werkstätte considered the design and production of all arts and crafts to be of equal importance.

Ref: Vienna, Österreichisches Museum für Angewandte Kunst, *Die Wiener Werkstätte,* p. 88.

108

Peter Behrens, *Feste des Lebens und der Kunst,*
eine Betrachtung des Theaters als Höchsten Kul-
tursymbols
Peter Behrens, illustrator
Dedicated to the "Künstler Kolonie" of Darmstadt
Leipzig, Eugen Diederichs, 1900

Decorated frontispiece, title-page, 2 borders, and initial by Peter Behrens. Printed by C. F. Winter-'schen Buchdruckerei, Darmstadt, in blue, brown, and red.

8⅝ x 7 in. Original gray wrappers, upper cover printed with title in black flanked with design by Behrens of gilt flames rising from urns.

Lent by the Harvard Theater Collection. Purchased from the bequest of Francis Brown Hayes

Many German artists of the Jugendstil were proficient in various media, like their English contemporaries. Peter Behrens, a pioneer of twentieth-century architecture, began as a painter and graphic artist and also designed for jewelry, glassware, porcelain, and furniture. In 1899 he joined six other artists, including J. M. Olbrich, in an artists' colony at Mathildenhöhe near Darmstadt, at the invitation of the Grand Duke Ernst Ludwig of Hesse. It is to this group that Behrens dedicated *Feste des Lebens und der Kunst.* Characteristic of Behrens and the Germans is the geometric control of the design, with the repetitive curvilinear forms subordinated to a strict framework. Behrens also designed alphabets and type, seen here in the decorated initial *S* and the simple Roman letters of the text.

DER KÜNSTLER-
KOLONIE IN
DARMSTADT
GEWIDMET

108. Peter Behrens. Dedication page for *Feste des Lebens und der Kunst*. 1900

This adds to the clarity of the pages, in contrast to the black-letter text accompanying his illustrations in *Der Bunte Vogel* (No. 103).

Ref: Loubier, *Die Neue Deutsche Buchkunst*, p. 27-28 ill.; Schauer, *Deutsche Buchkunst*, vol. 1, p. 43, vol. 2, pl. 6 ill.; Hofstätter, *Jugendstil Druckkunst*, p. 138; New York, The Museum of Modern Art, *Art Nouveau*, p. 166, p. 18 ill.

109

Johann Karl August Musaeus, *Die Buecher der Chronika der drei Schwestern*
Heinrich Lefler and *Joseph Urban*, illustrators
Berlin, J. A. Stargardt, 1900

Pictorial title-page with border by Lefler and Urban printed in black and gold floral pattern, lettered in black and red-brown, 6 full-page color plates, chapter headings, tailpieces, initial letters and decorative borders signed jointly with monogram *HL-JU*, printed in black or color with gold. Printed by the Reichsdruckerei.

15⅝ x 15¾ in. Blue cloth blocked with dark blue border stamped with circle device with three heraldic emblems in gold and red-brown, titled in black. End papers with floral repeat pattern in beige and gray on peach ground.

Gift of Peter A. Wick

Heinrich Lefler illustrated H. C. Andersen's *Die Prinzessin und der Schweinhirt* in 1897 and frequently collaborated with his brother-in-law Joseph Urban, for example, in J. K. A. Musaeus, *Rolands Knappen,* 1898. The size and sumptuousness of this children's book printed at the Imperial Printing Office in Berlin is of operatic scale. The illustrations reveal a national historical style common to books of epic chivalry in this period, but some plates, in dazzling color with lavish gold printing, show the attenuated linearity and symbolism of the Jugendstil.

110

Stefan George, *Der Teppich des Lebens und die Lieder von Traum und Tod mit einem Vorspiel*

Melchior Lechter, designer and illustrator
Berlin, Blaetter fuer die Kunst, 1900

Decorated title-page, 4 full-page illustrations, 3 different borders, and initials by Melchior Lechter, signed with initials *ML* and dated *1899*. Printed by Otto von Holten in red and black on gray paper.

14 x 14 in. Green cloth, upper cover stamped with repetition of title-page design with medallion of bird and two candelabra in blue by Lechter, signed with initials *ML*, and dated *1899*. This copy with inscription by Lechter on flyleaf. No. 227 of 300 copies.

Purchased from the George L. Lincoln Fund

Stefan George founded the Blaetter fuer die Kunst for the publication of his own works, and his friend Melchior Lechter illustrated all George's books from 1897 to 1907. Both men were influenced by the English Pre-Raphaelites and by William Morris. Lechter's work has a strong medieval character, apparent here in his use of Gothic arches. The Gothic was one of many sources of the Jugendstil, and in *Der Teppich des Lebens,* Lechter has transformed the flamboyant S-curves, interwoven with the thorn bush, into an expression of the new style.

Ref: New York, The Museum of Modern Art, *Art Nouveau,* p. 174; Loubier, *Die Neue Deutsche Buchkunst,* pl. 17-18 ill.; Schauer, *Deutsche Buchkunst,* vol. 1, p. 51-53; Hofstätter, *Jugendstil Druckkunst,* p. 147-148 ill.; Bremen, Kunsthalle, *Europäischer Jugendstil,* no. 166; Münster, Westfälischer Kunstverein, *Melchior Lechter,* no. 91-97, pl. 45-47 ill.

111

Stefan George, ed., *Maximin, ein Gedenkbuch*
Melchior Lechter, designer and illustrator
Berlin, Blaetter fuer die Kunst, 1907

Decorated title-page, border repeated on frontispiece framing photograph, 6 vignettes, border, and initial by Melchior Lechter, some signed with initials *ML* and dated *1906*. Printed by Otto von Holten in red and black.

13½ x 10¼ in. Original Japanese vellum, upper cover gilt-stamped with title and geometric design with flames in triangle by Lechter, signed with initials *ML*, lover cover gilt-stamped with medallion in triangle, edges gilt. No. 141 of 200 regular copies. Edition of 201 copies (200 regular, 1 on vellum).

Purchased from the bequest of Edwin Conant

Although based on a conventional arrangement, the details of Lechter's borders for *Maximin* contain elements of the Jugendstil in the nervous interlace and truncated forms. More experimental are the initials and vignettes, whose irregular shapes owe little to traditional sources. Lechter's graphic work is characterized by broad shapes, heavy lines, and sharp contrasts of black and white recalling fifteenth-century woodcuts.

Ref: New York, The Museum of Modern Art, *Art Nouveau*, p. 174; Schauer, *Deutsche Buchkunst*, vol. 1, p. 51-53, vol. 2, pl. 13 ill.; Hofstätter, *Jugendstil Druckkunst*, p. 146, 148 ill.; Münster, Westfälischer Kunstverein, *Melchior Lechter*, no. 107-116, pl. 111 ill.

112

Lothar Treuge, *Huldigungen*
Melchior Lechter, designer and illustrator
Berlin, Blaetter fuer die Kunst, 1908

Decorated title-page, frontispiece, vignettes, and border by Melchior Lechter, title-page and frontispiece signed with initials *ML* and dated *1908*. Printed by Otto von Holten in red and black.

12¾ x 9½ in. Original "parchment" boards, upper cover gilt-stamped with title and line border. No. 30 of 200 copies on india paper. Edition of 210 copies (10 on imperial japan, 200 on india).

Purchased from the Henry Wadsworth Longfellow Fund

Less medieval and more Jugendstil than Lechter's earlier illustrations (Nos. 110-111) are the pages of *Huldigungen*, architecturally framed with an order more Egyptian than classical. The frontispiece is without Lechter's usual heavy outlines, but with the same strong contrasts of black and white.

Ref: New York, The Museum of Modern Art, *Art Nouveau*, p. 174; Schauer, *Deutsche Buchkunst*, vol. 1, p. 51-53; Hofstätter, *Jugendstil Druckkunst*, p. 148; Münster, Westfälischer Kunstverein, *Melchior Lechter*, no. 124-125, pl. 53 ill.

113

Oscar Wilde, *Salome, Tragoedie in einem Akt*
Hedwig Lachman, translator
Marcus Behmer, illustrator
Leipzig, Insel-Verlag, 1903

Decorated double title-page and 10 illustrations by Marcus Behmer, some signed with initial *B*. Printed by Poeschel and Trepte.

8 x 6 in. Original Japanese vellum, upper cover gilt-stamped with title and design of iris by Behmer, dark gray end papers gilt-stamped with mantled figure. No. 48 of 50 copies on imperial japan.

Gift of Philip Hofer

Marcus Behmer's *Salome* of 1903 is greatly indebted to Aubrey Beardsley's treatment of 1894 (No. 27). The figures are executed with the same linear stylization, but Behmer's line is coarser. Striking as his images are, they lack the refinement and the fantasy that give significance to Beardsley's macabre sophistication.

Ref: New York, The Museum of Modern Art, *Art Nouveau*, p. 164; Schauer, *Deutsche Buchkunst*, vol. 1, p. 49, vol. 2, pl. 47 ill.; Hofstätter, *Jugendstil Druckkunst*, p. 157 ill.; Zürich, Kunstgewerbemuseum, *Druckkunst des Jugendstils*, no. 23, p. 39 ill.

114

Omar Khayyam, *Ruba'ijat*
G. D. Gribble, translator
Marcus Behmer, illustrator
Leipzig, Insel-Verlag, 1907

Decorated double title-page and initials by Marcus Behmer. Printed by Otto von Holten, Berlin, in green, gold, and black.

9½ x 6¾ in. Original green calf, upper cover gilt-stamped with title and stylized Persian foliate design by Behmer.
No. 17 of 50 copies on japan.

Gift of Peter A. Wick

Marcus Behmer's treatment of the *Ruba'ijat* is based on traditional interlaced designs, but varied, stretched, and elongated into Jugendstil forms. This is also true of the initials, especially the *E*, *M*, and *N*, constructed with deliberate distortions and irregularities.

Ref: New York, The Museum of Modern Art, *Art Nouveau*, p. 164; Loubier, *Die Neue Deutsche Buchkunst,* pl. 81-82 ill.; Hofstätter, *Jugendstil Druckkunst*, p. 157.

115

Friedrich Nietzsche, *Also Sprach Zarathustra,*
ein Buch für Alle und Keinen
Henry van de Velde, illustrator
Leipzig, Insel-Verlag, 1908

Title-page with ornament, added decorated double title-page, 4 full-page designs, vignettes, and ornaments by Henry van de Velde. Type fount designed by Georges Lemmen and cast under the supervision of Count Harry Kessler. Printed by W. Drugulin in dark reddish-purple, gold and black.

First copy: 14⅝ x 9¾ in. Original Japanese vellum, upper cover gilt-stamped with geometric design by van de Velde, spine gilt-stamped with title within ornamental frame; top edges gilt, white end papers with gilt geometric borders. No. 171 of 430 copies bound in Japanese vellum. Edition of 530 copies (100 bound in leather, 430 in Japanese vellum).

Purchased from the Caroline Miller Parker Fund

Second copy: No. 144 of 430 regular copies. Bound like first copy.

Lent by the Busch-Reisinger Museum

In 1901 Henry van de Velde was invited by the Grand Duke of Saxe-Weimar to head the Weimar School for Arts and Crafts, the predecessor of the Bauhaus, and he remained active and influential in Germany for many years. *Also Sprach Zarathustra* is his most monumental book design, very different in character from his slender Belgian volumes of the Nineties (Nos. 80 and 81), but created with similar abstract elements. The full-page designs are bold and dynamic, dramatically printed in deep reddish-purple and gold. Contrasting with these forceful pages are the typographic ones, with van de Velde's small gold designs forming a geometric framework for Lemmen's type, which was produced under Kessler's supervision. Van de Velde was closely associated with Kessler and designed books for his Cranach Press and furniture for his house.

Ref: Day, *Book Typography*, p. 27-28; New York, The Museum of Modern Art, *Art Nouveau,* p. 117, 183; Schauer, *Deutsche Buchkunst,* vol. 1, p. 61, vol. 2, pl. 16 ill.

116

Friedrich Nietzsche, *Ecce Homo*
Henry van de Velde, illustrator
Leipzig, Insel-Verlag, 1908

Decorated double title-page and ornaments by Henry van de Velde. Printed by Friedrich Richter in brown and black.

9½ x 7½ in. Original half Japanese vellum, gray boards, upper cover gilt-stamped with title in medallion designed by van de Velde, spine gilt-stamped with title; top edges gilt, brown end papers.
No. 291 of 1100 regular copies. Edition of 1250 copies (1100 regular, 150 on japan).

Purchased from the Caroline Miller Parker Fund

Smaller and quieter than the *Zarathustra* (No. 115), the *Ecce Homo* features a decorative title-page combining van de Velde's swelling abstract ornament with his own lettering. He also designed the ornaments, which, like the title-page, are printed in light brown, in contrast to the black of the letterpress.

Ref: Schauer, *Deutsche Buchkunst,* vol. 1, p. 34, vol. 2, pl. 15 ill.; Hofstätter, *Jugendstil Druckkunst,* p. 100 ill.

117

Friederich Hebbel, *Judith, eine Tragödie in 5 Akten*
Thomas Theodor Heine, illustrator and designer of binding
Munich, Hans von Weber, 1908

10 full-page illustrations by Heine printed in black on japan, signed with monogram *TTH*, 1 vignette and 9 head- and tailpieces printed in black on text pages. Printed by Poeschel & Trepte, Leipzig.

8½ x 7 in. Black cloth, upper cover gilt-stamped with panel ornament and title by Heine, signed lower left with monogram *TTH*; lower cover with similar panel ornament and publisher's monogram *HVW*. One of 1000 regular copies. Edition of 1100 copies (100 signed and numbered on imperial japan, 1000 on van Gelder with plates on japan).

Gift of Peter A. Wick

The Heine drawings in pen and india ink illustrating this text seem almost a spoof of the Beardsley style, but with their own mirthful convention of satirical cartoon.

Ref: Schauer, *Deutsche Buchkunst*, vol. 1, p. 25, 211, vol. 2, pl. 10 ill.; Hofstätter, *Jugendstil Druckkunst*, p. 180 ill.; Zürich, Kunstgewerbemuseum, *Druckkunst des Jugendstils*, p. 22, no. 95-97 ill.

118

Lafcadio Hearn, *Kwaidan, Seltsame Geschichten und Studien aus Japan*
Berta Franzos, translator
Emil Orlik, illustrator and designer of binding
Frankfurt am Main, Rütten & Loening, 1909

Decorated double title-page, 21 full-page illustrations, vignettes, ornaments and initials by Emil Orlik. Printed by Oscar Brandstetter, Leipzig.

8 x 5½ in. Original Japanese vellum, upper cover gilt-stamped with title and repetition of title-page design in gilt and black by Orlik, spine gilt- and black-stamped with title and stylized floral ornament; top edges gilt, cream end papers gilt

speckled, with design of stylized birds and author's initials *LH* in circle by Orlik.

Gift of Harris Kennedy

Emil Orlik, a native of Prague, who exhibited with the Vienna Secession and with the Wiener Werkstätte, traveled to Japan in 1900 and studied the technique of the Japanese woodcut. This influence, as well as a partiality for Japanese ornament and composition, is apparent in his treatment of *Kwaidan*. The oriental sources, however, were only the beginning of Orlik's design, for he combined the motifs in his own manner and transformed them by linear exaggeration into an expression of the Jugendstil.

Ref: Hofstätter, *Jugendstil Druckkunst*, p. 242-243 ill.

119

Vienna Secession, *Katalog der Kunst Ausstellung der Vereinigung Bildenden Künstler Österreichs*
Exhibition Catalogues no. 1, 5, 8, 10, 13, 14; 1898–1902

No. 1 (1898)
Vignettes by Adolf Böhm, Josef Hoffmann, Friedrich König, J. Victor Krämer, Koloman Moser, Karl Müller.
10⅝ x 4⅛ in. Terra cotta wrappers, upper cover printed with title and design of classical female warrior with shield by Gustav Klimt.

No. 5 (1899)
Vignettes by various Secession artists.
6¾ x 6 in. Green and white wrappers, upper cover printed with title within decorative framework by Josef Hoffmann.

No. 8 (1900)
Vignettes by Josef M. Auchentaller, Josef Hoffmann, Rudolf Jettmar, Friedrich König, Wilhelm List, Charles Rennie Mackintosh, Margaret Macdonald Mackintosh, Koloman Moser, Alfred Roller.
12½ x 3⅛ in. Red and white polka dot cloth, upper cover with gold and black printed label.

No. 10 (1901)
2 vignettes: 1 by Gustav Klimt, 1 by Joseph Maria Olbrich. Photographs of previous exhibitions.

116. Henry van de Velde.
Double title-page for
Ecce Homo. 1908

NIETZSCHE

6⅛ x4¾ in. Ochre wrappers, printed with geometric design in black by Josef Hoffmann, upper cover with title.

No. 13 (1902)
Geometric ornaments by Koloman Moser.
6⅜ x 5 in. Light blue wrappers, upper cover printed with geometric design in purple and black by Moser.

No. 14 (1902)
Klinger-Beethoven exhibition. Title-page by Alfred Roller, woodcuts by Ferdinand Andri, Rudolf Jettmar, Friedrich König, Max Kurzweil, Maximilian Lenz, Wilhelm List, Elena Luksch-Makovsky, Karl Moll, Koloman Moser, Felician von Myrbach, Emil Orlik, Ernst Stöhr; monograms and initials.
7 x 6⅛ in. Yellow wrappers, upper cover blind stamped with title.

Lent by Christian M. Nebehay (no. 1, 5, 8, 10, 13)
Gift of Peter A. Wick (no. 1 [2nd copy], 14)

The nineteen Viennese artists who withdrew in 1897 from the Künstlerhausgenossenschaft called their group the "Vereinigung bildender Künstler Österreichs." They came to be known as the "Secession," and the Viennese version of Art Nouveau as the "Secessionstil," since it first appeared in this milieu. *Ver Sacrum* (No. 120) was their official publication, and their first group exhibition took place in March, 1898. Joseph Maria Olbrich designed the Secession building, in which the second exhibition opened on November 12, 1898. A small vignette of this building appears in the catalogue of the tenth exhibition. Gustav Klimt, the first president, designed the covers of the first exhibition catalogue, which is decorated with vignettes by various members of the group. Josef Hoffmann designed the covers for the fifth and tenth exhibitions, and Koloman Moser for the thirteenth. Each catalogue contains lists of regular and honorary members, including several other European and English artists. Of particular influence in Vienna were the Scottish "four Macs," who were prominently included in the eighth exhibition in 1900. Both Charles Rennie Mackintosh and his wife Margaret Macdonald Mackintosh contributed vignettes

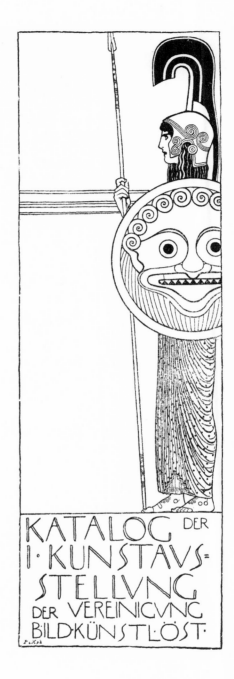

Josef Hoffmann. Cover for Vienna Secession, *Katalog* No. 5. 1899

to the catalogue, and work by his partner Herbert MacNair and his wife, Frances Macdonald Mac-Nair, was included.

Ref: *Wien um 1900,* p. 44, no. 299, 301, 302; Nebehay, *Klimt Dokumentation,* p. 139-140, 200, 231, 239, 259, 277 ill.

120
Ver Sacrum,
Organ der Vereinigung Bildender Kuenstler
Österreichs
Vienna, 1898-1903. 6 volumes.

9¾ x 9¼ in. Full contemporary cloth, curvilinear pattern woven in blue and gold, upper cover gilt-stamped with title and date.

Purchased from the bequest of Amy Lowell

Ver Sacrum was the official organ of the Vienna Secession (No. 119), the group founded in 1897 with the painter Gustav Klimt as president and the architects Josef Hoffmann and Joseph Maria Olbrich leading members. Their work and that of Koloman Moser is particularly prominent in the early numbers of the new periodical, of which six volumes were published between 1898 and 1903. The literary editors of the first volume were Hermann Bahr and Max Burckhard, and the publishers Gerlach and Schenk of Vienna. The second volume appeared with the imprint of E. A. Seeman, Leipzig and was printed by Breitkopf and Härtel in that

city. In this second volume the name of Franz Zweybrück appears as editor, with Friedrich König, Koloman Moser, Joseph M. Olbrich and Alfred Roller as art editors. During the remaining four years of its publication, there was considerable shifting of editorial and artistic direction. The first cover of 1898 is by Alfred Roller, the second by Koloman Moser, and the third by Gustav Klimt. The first cover of 1899 reproduces Olbrich's drawing of his noted Secession building in Vienna, with the inscription over the door, "Der Zeit ihre Kunst, Der Kunst ihre Freiheit." *Ver Sacrum* not only published the work of the Viennese group, but also other Europeans in whom they were interested, such as Walter Crane, Alphonse Mucha, Eugène Grasset, Théo van Rysselberghe, Fernand Khnopff, and the Scottish "four Macs." The generally geometric and simplified character of the Austrian Jugendstil is apparent in the pages of *Ver Sacrum,* whose distinctive square format and high graphic quality make it not only the most important expression of this school, but one of the most significant journals of the period.

Ref: Madsen, *Art Nouveau,* p. 130-131, 181, 183-185, 217; New York, The Museum of Modern Art, *Art Nouveau,* p. 75, 117, 137; Hofstätter, *Jugendstil Druckkunst,* p. 209-240 ill.; The Houghton Library, *Vienna 1888-1938,* no. 65.

120a and 120b
Gustav Klimt, *Initial "D"*
Drawing for *Ver Sacrum,* I, 1898

Pencil, pen and india ink,
signed lower right in pen: *Gustav Klimt.*
7¾ x 3¹⁵⁄₁₆ in. (sheet)

Gustav Klimt, *Study for Unpublished Vignette*
Drawing for *Ver Sacrum,* ca. 1898
Pencil, pen and india ink
4¹⁵⁄₁₆ x 3⅝ in. (sheet)

Lent by Christian M. Nebehay

These two ornamental vignettes for *Ver Sacrum* show Klimt's flat Grecian style of the period with the sardonic, mask-like shades of his facial types.

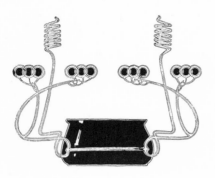

120. Koloman Moser. Illustration for *Ver Sacrum*, 1901, p. 356

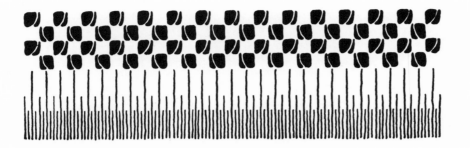

GEORGE MINNE.

MAN hat merkwürdige Sachen in Wien über die Minne=Ausstellung gelesen und gehört; deprimie=rend merkwürdig, grotesk und leider so roh, als wären wir noch in der Zeit der Kreuzzüge. Wo bleibt der berühmte Fortschritt? Man fährt immer schneller,

von Banalem umgeben, wir müssen Banales sehen und thun, so will es unser Erdenlos. Gebenedeit seien die Augen=blicke, wo uns anderes geschieht. ☺☺☺

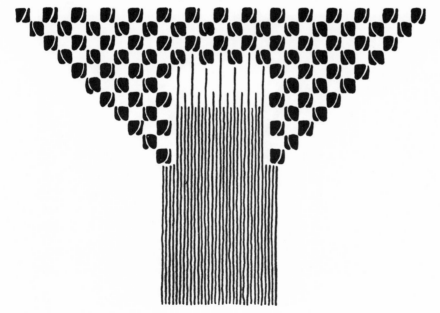

120. Koloman Moser.
Headpiece and tailpiece for
Ver Sacrum, 1901, p. 31, 41

Klimt did several initial letters for *Ver Sacrum* which set the model for others designed by Koloman Moser, Alfred Roller, Josef Hoffmann and Fernand Khnopff.

Ref: *Ver Sacrum*, I, 1898, Heft 3, p. 23; Nebehay, *Klimt Dokumentation*, p. 151 ill.; Nebehay, *Klimt exh. cat.*, no. 26.

121

[Joseph Maria Olbrich], *Ideen von Olbrich*
Joseph Maria Olbrich, designer
Vienna, Gerlach & Schenk, n. d.

Decorated title-page, 8 color plates, reproductions of drawings, photographs of architecture and interiors by Olbrich.

7½ x 8⅞ in. Loose plates in green wrappers, upper cover with title and ornamental border in black and yellow by Olbrich, flap with stylized floral design in yellow.

Gift of Peter A. Wick

Olbrich's *Ideen* pictured here are for the most part architectural in character, reproduced from drawings and from photographs of completed buildings. Prominently featured are the Villa Friedmann near Vienna, the artists' colony at Mathildenhöhe near Darmstadt, and rooms for the Vienna Secession and Paris exhibitions. The *Ideen* first appeared in 1900, and an enlarged edition in 1904.

Ref: New York, The Museum of Modern Art, *Art Nouveau*, p. 177-178; Darmstadt, Hessisches Landesmuseum, *Joseph M. Olbrich*, p. 3

122

Wilhelm Holzamer, *Spiele*
Joseph Maria Olbrich, illustrator
Dedicated to the Grand Duke Ernst Ludwig of Hesse
Leipzig, Eugen Diederichs, 1901

9 illustrations by J. M. Olbrich. Printed by the Spamersche Buchdruckerei in dark blue.

8 x 5½ in. Original dark red wrappers with cord,

upper cover gilt-stamped with geometric design and lettered title by Olbrich, signed *Olbrich*.

Lent by the Busch-Reisinger Museum,
Gift of Charles L. Kuhn

Like Behrens' *Feste des Lebens und der Kunst* (No. 108), Olbrich's designs for Holzamer's *Spiele* were created at the artists' colony at Mathildenhöhe, near Darmstadt, under the patronage of the Grand Duke Ernst Ludwig of Hesse. Olbrich was a leader of the Vienna Secession in 1897 and had contributed to *Ver Sacrum* (No. 120) and designed the Vienna Secession building before joining the Darmstadt group, of which he was one of the most influential members. He designed most of the buildings for the colony and a good deal of furniture. His decorations for *Spiele,* which have an architectural character, with some interior design and furniture, are flat, two dimensional, and delicately conceived. Typical of the Vienna Secession is their geometric quality, for the free curves and irregular shapes are subordinated to strict horizontal and vertical boundaries.

Ref: New York, The Museum of Modern Art, *Art Nouveau,* p. 177-178; Darmstadt, Hessisches Landesmuseum, *Joseph M. Olbrich,* p. 168, no. 219 ill.

123

Ars Nova,
Hervorragende Werke der Bildenden Künste
Koloman Moser, designer
Felician Freiherr von Myrbach, art editor
Introduction by Julius Meier-Graefe (vol. I), Frans Servaes (vol. II)
Vienna, Leipzig, Budapest; Max Herzig, 1901-1902
2 volumes.

Title-page (vol. I) with decorated border in leaf pattern after design by Koloman Moser, printed in ochre; head- and tailpieces and borders with square repeat pattern of stylized rose in yellow-ochre; 45 heliogravure reproductions (each vol.) of paintings by Aman-Jean, Besnard, Carrière, Klimt, Klinger, Repin, Rodin, Uhde, Zuloaga, etc. (vol. I); Chase, Hofmann, Klinger, Laurens, Le Sidaner, Robinson, Shannon, Thoma, Toorop, etc. (vol. II). Each plate blind-stamped with monogram *Ars Nova MCMI.* Printed by Max Herzig & Co., Vienna. Plates printed by F. A. Brockhaus, Leipzig.

17¾ x 13¾ in. Red cloth with overall rose pattern by Koloman Moser printed in silver; center panel blocked in silver with title and date. End papers

with stylized rose stem and bayberry pattern printed in dark ochre on light.

Gift of Peter A. Wick

These two weighty volumes of *Ars Nova* are notable mainly for the lavish production of the binding on Volume I designed by Koloman Moser, with stylized roses in full bloom printed in silver on red ground, the outline of the petals creating a swirling overall pattern. This cover, however, smacks somewhat of the heavy pretentiousness found in much official art.

Ref: Graz, Neue Galerie, *Koloman Moser* exh. cat., no. 153.

124

Hugo Schwerdtner, *Die Stumme Seele, ein Märchen aus der Innenwelt*
Berthold Löffler, illustrator and designer of binding
Vienna and Leipzig, Wilhelm Braunmüller, 1901

3 vignettes by Berthold Löffler, signed with monogram *Lö.* Printed by Friedrich Jasper.

8⅝ x 5⅞ in. Original mottled green cloth, upper cover gilt-stamped with title and design of spider's web and small red flowers by Löffler, signed with monogram *BLö.*

Gift of Peter A. Wick

Löffler's little vignettes are Jugendstil compositions of floral forms. With linear exaggeration he has fused the spider's web and the Gothic lettering of the cover into an asymmetrical composition.

Ref: Hofstätter, *Jugendstil Druckkunst,* p. 244.

125

Arthur Schnitzler, *Reigen, Zehn Dialoge*
Berthold Löffler, designer
Vienna, Wiener Verlag, 1903

Decorated title-page, full-page design repeated several times, and vignettes by Berthold Löffler. Printed by Hofbuchdruckerei Fr. Winiker Schickardt, Brünn.

7½ x 5⅜ in. Original gray wrappers, upper cover printed with title and geometric design in black and white by Löffler. Modern half red morocco.

Purchased from the George L. Lincoln Fund

The first published edition of *Reigen* is also one of the early publications of the Wiener Verlag. Löffler's title-page is characteristic of the simple geometric tendencies of the Wiener Werkstätte, which he later joined, but even these forms are drawn with some of the irregularity and tension of the Jugendstil.

Ref: Hofstätter, *Jugendstil Druckkunst,* p. 244; The Houghton Library, *Vienna 1888-1938,* no. 16; *Wien um 1900,* no. 436.

126
Felix Salten, *Gustav Klimt,*
Gelegentliche Anmerkungen
Berthold Löffler, designer
Vienna and Leipzig, Wiener Verlag, 1903

Decorated title-page with ornaments by Berthold Löffler. Printed by W. Schenkler in yellow, green, and black.

6⅛ x 5⅞ in. Original printed wrappers with geometric design in green, black, and yellow by Löffler. Upper cover with title lettered in white on black.

Gift of Peter A. Wick

Löffler designed this little catalogue for Klimt's first one-man show in Vienna.

Ref: Nebehay, *Klimt Dokumentation,* p. 228.

127
Schwarz auf Weiss,
Wiener Autoren den Wiener Kunstgewerbeschul-
ern zu ihren Feste am 6 Februar, 1902
Vienna, Wiener Kunstgewerbeschule; Leipzig, Heinrich Blomer, 1902

Otto M. Miethke and *Bertha Czegka,* designers of covers

Illustrations by 18 different artists. Printed by Adolf Holzhausen.

First copy: 6½ x 3¾ in. Vienna issue. Original lavender wrappers printed with geometric design by Otto M. Miethke in black and white, upper cover with title, black and white geometric end papers.

Gift of Peter A. Wick

Second copy: 6½ x 3¾ in. Vienna issue. Covers like first copy.

Purchased from the Charles Minot Fund

Third copy: 6½ x 3¾ in. Leipzig issue. Pictorial upper cover of flower seller by Bertha Czegka, signed with monogram *BC,* lavender borders; lower cover and end papers like first and second copies.

Gift of Curt H. Reisinger

The Secessionstil in Vienna influenced the official schools, as seen in this lighthearted little festival publication of the Vienna School of Applied Arts. It presents humor and caricature with an incisive, stylized rhythmic line and silhouette.

Ref: Kornfeld und Klipstein, *Jugendstil,* no. 667.

128. Berthold Löffler. Illustration for *Theater und Kabarett Fledermaus*. 1907

Theater und Kabarett Fledermaus
Programs no. 1 and 2
Vienna, Wiener Werkstätte, 1907

No. 1: 4 illustrations: 1 by Oskar Kokoschka (signed with initials *OK*), 1 by Berthold Löffler, 2 by Fritz Zeymer (signed with monogram *FZ*). Design and borders by Carl Otto Czeschka. Printed by Chwala in color.

9⅝ x 9¼ in. Wrappers with multi-color circular and geometric designs by Czeschka, signed with monogram *COC*.

No. 2: 8 illustrations by Moritz Jung, signed with monogram *MJ*. Design and borders by Czeschka. Printed by Chwala in black.

9⅝ x 9¼ in. Wrappers with upper cover printed with design of performing monkeys on black ground by Jung, signed with monogram *MJ*.

Gift of Philip Hofer

The architect Josef Hoffmann, one of the leaders of the Vienna Secession, founded the Wiener Werkstätte in 1903. Like the English Arts and Crafts movement, this new organization concerned itself with design in all fields, a preoccupation of many Jugendstil artists. Stylistically, the Wiener Werkstätte evolved a geometric simplicity of form, influential in later twentieth-century developments. The interior of the Kabarett Fledermaus, opened in 1907, was designed by Hoffmann. Peter Altenberg, Hermann Bahr, and Franz Blei were the literary guides for this experimental theatre, and Czeschka, Hoffmann, Klimt, Kokoschka, and Löffler were among the artists who designed productions. These two programs were the only ones published.

Ref: Hoffstätter, *Jugendstil Druckkunst*, p. 249 ill.; Waissenberger, *Buchkunst aus Wien*, p. 21; *Wien um 1900*, p. 74, no. 561-562, pl. 67; Vienna, Österreichisches Museum für Angewandte Kunst, *Die Wiener Werkstätte*, no. 451-452, pl. 64-65 ill.

129

Oskar Kokoschka, *Die Traeumenden Knaben*

Oskar Kokoschka, illustrator
Dedicated to Gustav Klimt
Vienna, Wiener Werkstätte, 1908

10 lithographs by Oskar Kokoschka, several signed with initials *OK*. Printed by Berger and Chwala, with 8 lithographs in color and 2 in black and white.

9⅜ x 11 in. Original white cloth, upper cover with printed white label with title and figure composition.

Gift of Philip Hofer

Kokoschka's versatility has shown itself in literature as well as painting and graphic arts, and he was only twenty-two when this first book was published by the Wiener Werkstätte. He also designed postcards for the group and contributed to the Kabarett Fledermaus programs (No. 128). The influence of folk art and the harsh outlines of early woodcuts are apparent in the pages of *Die Traeumenden Knaben*, but modernized and exaggerated into a highly personal style. Kurt Wolff reissued 275 copies in 1917 in Munich.

Ref: Schauer, *Deutsche Buchkunst*, vol. 1, p. 217, vol. 2, pl. 115 ill.; Boston Museum-Harvard College Library, *The Artist and the Book*, no. 147 ill.; Hofstätter, *Jugendstil Druckkunst*, p. 246, 250 ill.; *Wien um 1900*, no. 398; Bremen, Kunsthalle, *Europäischer Jugendstil*, no. 589; Vienna, Österreichisches Museum für Angewandte Kunst, *Die Wiener Werkstätte*, no. 453, pl. 66 ill.; Hofmann, *Turning Points in Twentieth Century Art, 1890-1917*, p. 36-37; The Houghton Library, *Vienna 1888-1938*, no. 71.

130

Lucian, *Die Hetaerengespraeche*
Franz Blei, translator
Gustav Klimt, illustrator
Leipzig, Julius Zeitler, 1907

15 reproductions of drawings by Gustav Klimt. Printed by W. Drugulin.

14¼ x 11⅜ in. Original rose cloth, upper cover gilt-stamped with title lettered by Klimt. No. 411 of 450 copies.

Purchased from the Constantius Fund

As leader and first president of the Secession, Gustav Klimt was one of the most prominent artists in Vienna at the turn of the century. Primarily a painter, he did a certain amount of graphic work, especially for *Ver Sacrum* (No. 120). The drawings for the Lucian of thin, emaciated nudes are invested with a perverse eroticism found in many figure drawings of this period.

Ref: New York, The Museum of Modern Art, *Art Nouveau*, p. 173; The Houghton Library, *Vienna 1885-1938*, no. 67; Hofstätter, *Jugendstil Druckkunst*, p. 214; Nebehay, *Klimt Dokumentation*, p. 158, 159, 359f., ill.; Nebehay, *Klimt exh. cat.*, no. 33.

131

Die Nibelungen (*Gerlach's Jugendbücherei*, vol. 22)
Franz Keim, editor
C. O. Czeschka, illustrator
Vienna and Leipzig, Gerlach und Wiedling, 1909

Decorated title-page and frontispiece by Czeschka with spiraling ribbon decoration enclosing block

lettering printed in black; 8 double-page color illustrations with much gold printing, signed with *remarque*; vignettes, decorated initial, head- and tailpieces, printed in black. Printed by Christoph Reisser's Sohne.

6 x 5¼ in. Gray cloth with title in small central square blocked in black, end papers with ruffled vertical stripes in blue on white.

Gift of Peter A. Wick

This children's book from a popular series of thirty-four volumes called *Gerlach's Jugendbücherei,* in uniform format, each by different illustrators, and published between 1902 and 1920, is the most striking Jugendstil example of the set. The mosaic-like flat patches of blue, black and gold with occasional red accents, much in the Secession formula, form a strong rich background for a variety of Czeschka's unusual geometric patterns.

Ref: Hofstätter, *Jugendstil Druckkunst,* p. 244-245 ill.: Ingo Nebehay, "Gerlach's Jugendbucherei"; Waissenberger, *Buchkunst aus Wien*, p. 23, ill. foll. p. 24.

UNITED STATES

A is for Art of the age-end variety
We Decadents simply can't get a satiety
Gelett Burgess

132

Robert Herrick, *Selections from the Hesperides and Noble Numbers*
Edwin A. Abbey, illustrator
Dedicated to Alfred Parsons
New York, Harper & Brothers, 1882

Pictorial title-page with wood-engraving after drawing by Abbey, signed lower left *F. Delorme sc.*, 42 full-page wood-engravings; initial letter and numerous head- and tailpieces printed in wood-engraving after Abbey. Printed by the Leadenhall Press (Field & Tuer), London.

11¾ x 8⅞ in. Beige cloth, probably designed by Abbey with radiating sun blocked in gold, floating flowers in light olive-green extending around spine and lower cover, lettered in red and black.

Gift of Peter A. Wick

The cover design of this book, far in advance of Edwin Austin Abbey's narrative-style illustrations, is an early manifestation of Art Nouveau influence from across the Atlantic, in the somewhat vibrating, floating design, in the choice of green, gold and red on a pale beige cloth, and in the new freedom of hand-lettering.

Ref: Lewis, *The Twentieth Century Book,* p. 10 ill.

133

Nathaniel Hawthorne, *The Marble Faun*
Boston, Houghton, Mifflin and Co., 1889. 2 volumes.

Illustrated with photogravures (vol. 1: 27 photogravures; vol. 2: 24 photogravures). Printed by the Riverside Press, Cambridge, Mass.

9 x 6⅛ in. Full vellum, upper and lower covers stamped in gold with stylized iris over network of tiny hearts and fleurs-de-lis, arranged in square blocks. Copy no. 11 of 150 copies of the large paper edition.

Gift of Arthur Stuart Walcott

It was about this time that Mr. H. O. Houghton

brought over English and Continental binders and set up his own bindery.

Ref: Browne, *A Bibliography of Hawthorne*, p. 47.

134

Richard Doddridge Blackmore, *Fringilla, or Tales in Verse*
Will Bradley, illustrator
Cleveland, The Burrow Brothers Co., 1895

Pictorial frontispiece and title-page by Bradley printed in black with lettering in red and black; 9 full-page illustrations, decorative borders and initials in woodcut designed by Bradley, some signed *B* in the block. Printed by John Wilson & Son, University Press, Cambridge, with text in red and black.

9⅛ x 6¼ in. Half tan linen, blue boards, with upper and lower cover design by Bradley, printed in red and black. End papers decorated with pictorial panels by Bradley in pale green. No. 174 of 600 numbered copies on handmade paper with watermark *RUISDAEL*.

Gift of Prof. F. W. Taussig

Blackmore is more familiar as the author of *Lorna Doone*. In comparison with the English edition of the same year illustrated by Louis Fairfax-Muckley (No. 36) of the Birmingham School, America and Bradley come out on top: first, in the manner in which he has assimilated the influence of Whistler, Beardsley and Morris and turned it to his own use; and second, as a most imaginative and inventive designer both in decoration and illustration. The cover design with the sinuous maiden and tree is related to the cover of the November issue of *Bradley: His Book* (No. 136) and to his Peacock posters.

Ref: Huntington Library, *Will Bradley* exh. cat., p. 12, no. 4; New York, The Museum of Modern Art, *Art Nouveau,* p. 165; Charteris, "Zeitgenoessische Englishe Novellisten," ill. opp. p. 344; Hofstätter, *Jungendstil Druckkunst,* p. 78, 79; Hiatt, "Designs by Will H. Bradley."

135

Emerson Hough, *The Singing Mouse Stories*
Will Bradley, designer of cover; *W. S. Fields,*
illustrator
New York, Forest and Stream Publishing Co., 1895

Marginal illustrations by W. S. Fields. Colophon
of harp, hands and mouse by Bradley. Printed by
Geo. E. Cole & Co., Chicago.

7 x 3¾ in. Green linen, gilt-stamped with design of
girl with harp by Bradley; lower cover, singing
mouse.

Bequest of Susan Greene Dexter

This little book is notable for the elongated simplicity of the cover design and the charming lower
cover of the singing mouse. Bradley manages to
get away with designs that suggest but elude mannerism.

Ref: *Bradley: His Book,* p. 55.

136

[Will Bradley], *Bradley: His Book*
Will Bradley, editor, designer and illustrator
Springfield, Massachusetts, The Wayside Press
1896-1897. 2 volumes, 7 numbers.

Reproductions of drawings, posters and book illus-
trations by Edward Penfield, Maxfield Parrish,
Burne-Jones, William Morris, Henri de Toulouse-
Lautrec and Aubrey Beardsley with many original
designs by Will Bradley. Printed by the Wayside
Press, Springfield, Mass.

Vol. I. (1896): 10⅛ x 5⅛ in. 4 numbers in original
wrappers, upper and lower cover designs in color by
Bradley.
May, No. 1: Upper cover, design of flowering
tree in green, red and black on gray paper; lower
cover, advertisement for the Twin Comet Lawn
Sprinkler Co. showing fashionably dressed young
lady with revolving sprinkler behind her.
June, No. 2: Upper cover, abstract design of espa-
liered rose tree in ochre and black on buff paper;

lower cover, advertisement for Hartford Rubber
Works.
August, No. 4: Upper cover, design of climbing
roses in burnt sienna on cream paper; lower cover,
advertisement for Crocker's Mfg. Co. 14 full-page
and 28 half-page illustrations by Bradley for his
extravaganza *Beauty and the Beast.*

Vol. II (1896-1897): 11 x 8 in. 3 numbers in original
wrappers.
November, No. 1: Upper cover, in black and brown
design of standing girl in clinging drapery with
elongated peacock; design repeated on lower
cover. Includes a *Primer of Ornament Design*
by Bradley.
December, No. 2: Upper cover, abstract design of
holly leaf in dark green and red on light olive
paper; lettering in brown.
January, No. 3: Upper cover, title in deep brown
Gothic lettering; lower cover, advertisement for
Mittineague Paper Co.

Gift of Dr. J. R. Chadwick

In this publication, which was his first entirely
independent venture of this kind, many of Will
Bradley's truly great gifts appear as designer,
typographer, layout man and illustrator of books
and posters, as well as advertisements. His *Beauty
and the Beast,* while bowing in influence to
Beardsley, has much that is both striking and original. Bradley was a regular contributor to *The
Chap-Book* which first appeared in semi-monthly
issues, published by Stone & Kimball in Chicago.
He also contributed twelve cover designs for
The Inland Printer, another Chicago publication.

Ref: New York, The Museum of Modern Art, *Art Nouveau,* p. 165-166; Huntington Library, *Will Bradley* exh.
cat., p. 13, no. 9.

137

Stephen Crane, *War is Kind*
Will Bradley, illustrator
New York, Frederick A. Stokes Company, 1899

Title-page, 22 cuts, including 6 full-page, designed by Will Bradley. Printed by Will Bradley,
University Press, Cambridge and New York.

137. Will Bradley. Cover for *War is Kind.* 1899

8½ x 5½ in. Gray boards, upper cover stamped in black with design and title and signed upper left corner *BRADLEY*. Printed on gray laid paper.

Gift of Chester Noyes Greenough

This beautifully designed book, unlike most of Bradley's work, has more than a tinge of the exotic, as if admitting to a certain pictorial decadence parallel to the sophisticated disillusion of Crane's verses.

Do not weep, maiden, for war is kind.
Because your lover threw wild hands toward
    the sky
And the affrighted steed ran on alone,
Do not weep.
War is kind.

Ref: The Huntington Library, *Will Bradley*, exh. cat., p. 13, no. 9.

138
Gertrude Smith, *The Arabella and Araminta Stories*
Introduction by Mary E. Wilkins
Ethel Reed, illustrator
Boston, Copeland and Day (The Yellow Hair Library), 1895

Decorated title-page by Ethel Reed in two variants, printed in orange and black and green and black; multiple impressions of the 15 illustrations and the end papers printed on various papers and in various colored inks. Front and back end papers autographed in pen by the authors; back end paper in addition bears the *remarque* of the artist. Printed by John Wilson and Son, Cambridge, Mass.

17⅝ x 12 in. Half black morocco, batik cotton cloth in deep blue, rust and cream. One of an edition of 15 copies printed on royal Japanese paper.

Harvard College Library purchase

The fascination of this book lies in the great variety of proof impressions enclosed within one binding. Such variety of papers and experimentation with color printing are rare in a bound vol-

ume. Ethel Reed's designs have a bouncy "Beardsley" look all her own, which point to the influence of the more subtle and sensitive Englishman, as well as of the boisterous Bradley.

Ref: *Bradley: His Book,* July, p. 74-76; "The Work of Miss Ethel Reed," p. 230-236.

139
Max Beerbohm, *The Works of Max Beerbohm*
Margaret Armstrong, designer of binding
New York, Charles Scribner's Sons, 1896

Unillustrated.

7⅛ x 4⅝ in. Brown cloth, upper cover decorated with design of butterflies and circular globes surrounded by looped tracery, stamped in gilt and white. Signed by Margaret Armstrong with monogram *MA* lower right corner.

Gift of Albert E. Gallatin

The Art Nouveau "leit-motifs" of globe, butterfly and loop are all here combined with great restraint and feminine precision.

Ref: Gullans & Espey, *A Checklist of Trade Binding designed by Margaret Armstrong*, no. 22.

140
Paul Leicester Ford, *A Checked Love Affair and the Cortelyou Feud*
George Wharton Edwards and *Harrison Fisher*, illustrators
Margaret Armstrong, designer of binding
New York, Dodd, Mead and Company, 1903

Decorated title-page, publishers' device, list of illustrations, half-titles, borders, and colophon by George Wharton Edwards in green, yellow and black border designs. 4 illustrations in photogravure by Harrison Fisher. Printed by University Press, John Wilson and Son, Cambridge.

8¾ x 7⅝ in. Olive-green cloth. Upper cover designed by Margaret Armstrong, stamped in light and dark green and white floral design with author's name in white; title in gold.

Gift of Mrs. Hector J. Hughes

Horns of plenty from which climb yellow roses, cherubs, columns terminating in Roman lamps and, most ingenious of all, butterflies whose wings are sheer Art Nouveau in pattern and whose torch-like bodies are decorated with black hearts and terminate in eternal flames rather than earthly antennae —all these make up Mr. Edwards' repertoire. He excelled in a most charming way at a time when the crowded field of illustrators of novels and love stories rarely rose above their banal and saccharine subjects.

141
William Channing Gannet(t), *The House Beautiful*
Frank Lloyd Wright, designer
River Forest, Illinois, The Auvergne Press, 1896-1897

Decorated double title-page by Frank Lloyd Wright with horizontal frieze of "caryatid" youths supporting letter panel printed in red, enframed in intricate mosaic borders printed in black; ornamental borders and chapter headings in black with frequent border ornaments in red. Colophon with press mark. Printed privately at the Auvergne Press by William Herman Winslow and Frank Lloyd Wright. Brochure of 12 photogravures of dried field plants printed on china paper, sewn into flyleaf.

First copy: 13⅝ x 11⅛ in. Half brown calf, gilt-stamped, with green paper over boards, lettered in gold, top edges gilt. No. 10 of 90 numbered copies signed by Wright and Winslow.

Gift of Alan Winslow

Second copy: 13⅝ x 11⅛ in. No. 80 of regular edition. Bound like first copy. This copy with inserted autograph letter:

Samuel R. Morrill
Edward Morrill and Son
1252 Massachusetts Avenue
Cambridge 38
Massachusetts

My dear Mr. Morrill: Yes, my first work of the kind: an amateur feeling for a decorative pattern to harmonize with the type of the text — looking for it in the seed pods of weeds growing all about. The dried weeds were photographed and the photographs added to the fly-leaf of the book in a little brochure. Winslow and I did the printing ourselves in the basement of the house I designed for him.

The book was bound in Chicago by the leading binder of the time whose name escapes me. If you find several copies, we have but one and would like to acquire another.

Sincerely yours,

Frank Lloyd Wright   *September 27, 1949*

Harvard College Library, Department of Printing and Graphic Arts

The subtitle reads: "The House Beautiful * * * in a setting designed by Frank Lloyd Wright and printed by hand at the Auvergne Press in River Forest by William Herman Winslow and Frank Lloyd Wright during the winter months of the year eighteen hundred ninety six and seven * * *." Winslow was the grandfather of the donor, owner of the Winslow Ornamental Iron Works, who had given Frank Lloyd Wright his first independent architectural commission, the "Winslow House" in River Forest, 1893. The Winslow House itself had a rich terra-cotta frieze running around the exterior.
The intricate ornamental designs of *The House Beautiful* are the linear geometric products of the architect's T-square, triangle and compass, and they show Wright's original and complex imagination for decoration. This is not the foliated rhythm of Louis Sullivan's ornament, nor is it slavishly imitative of Turkish or Persian mosaic. It is a totally graphic design in Wright's favorite black and red, and sets the style for the format and decoration of most of his later published works. Wright was

no iconoclast, and this book recalls his early statement: "In architecture, expressive changes of surface, emphasis of line, and especially textures of material or imaginative patterns may go to make facts more eloquent—forms more significant."
On a prefatory page is printed a dedicatory verse: "With nature-warp of naked weed by printer-craft imprisoned, we weave this interlinear web, a rhythmic changing play of ordered space and image seeking trace our fabric makes, to clothe with chastity and grace our author's gentle word. Appreciation of the beauty in his work we weave,—in part ourselves to please, yet may we better fare, and, weaving so, with you our pleasure share."

Ref: Hitchcock, *In the Nature of Materials*, p. 23-24, fig. 25-28; Wright, *An Autobiography*, p. 125; Wright, *On Architecture*, p. 144.

142
Elbert Hubbard, *White Hyacinths*

Elbert Hubbard, designer
East Aurora, New York, Elbert Hubbard, 1907

Decorated double title-page with floral border by Elbert Hubbard in olive-green and black, signed with monogram *EH*, title in orange; vignettes, initials and colophon by Hubbard in olive-green and black.

7¼ x 4¼ in. Brown suede, upper cover stamped with design incorporating title and author.

Lent by David R. Godine

Avoidance of the elaborate in design results in a fresh if somewhat studied simplicity in this small book. It was the influence of William Morris that led Hubbard to found an artists' colony and private press.

Ref: Lane, *Elbert Hubbard*.

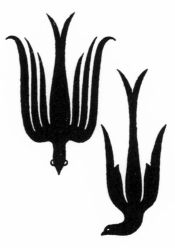

Selected Bibliography

Abdy, Jane. *The French Poster*. London, 1969.

Albi, Palais de la Berbie; Paris, Petit Palais. *Centenaire de Toulouse-Lautrec*. Albi-Paris, 1964.

Alexandre, Arsène. *The Modern Poster*. New York, 1895.

Amaya, Mario. *Art Nouveau*. London, 1966.

Arts Council of Great Britain. *James McNeill Whistler* [exh. cat.]. [London, 1960].

Aslin, Elizabeth. *The Aesthetic Movement, Prelude to Art Nouveau*. London, 1969.

Babington, Percy L. *Bibliography of the Writings of John Addington Symonds*. London, 1925.

Balston, Thomas. *The Cambridge University Press Collection of Private Press Types: Kelmscott, Ashendene, Eragny, Cranach*. Cambridge, 1951.

Battersby, Martin. *Art Nouveau*. London, 1969.

Baughman, Roland. *The Centenary of Arthur Rackham's Birth, an Appreciation of his Genius and a Catalogue of his Original Sketches, Drawings and Paintings in the Berol Collection*. New York, 1967.

Bodenhausen, E. von. "Das Englische Buch," *Pan*, II (1896), 337-340.

Bogan, Louise and Roget, Elizabeth. *The Journals of Jules Renard*. New York, 1964.

Boston, Museum of Fine Arts and Harvard College Library. *The Artist and the Book 1860-1960 in Western Europe and the United States*. Boston [1961].

Bradley, Will. *Bradley: his Book*. Springfield, Mass., 1896-1897.

Bremen, Kunsthalle, *Europäischer Jugendstil* [exh. cat.]. Bremen, 1965.

Brown University Library. *William Morris and the Kelmscott Press*. Providence, 1960.

Browne, Nina A. *A Bibliography of Nathaniel Hawthorne*. Boston and New York, 1895.

Brussels, Musées Royaux de Beaux-Arts; Otterlo, Rijksmuseum Kröller-Müller. *Le Groupe des XX et son Temps*. Brussels, 1962.

Carteret, L. *Le Trésor du Bibliophile, Livres illustrés modernes, 1875-1945*. 5 vols. Paris, 1946-1948.

Charteris, Archibald. "Zeitgenoessische Englishe Novellisten," *Pan*, II (1896), 341-344.

Crane, Walter. *The Claims of Decorative Art*. London, 1892.

Crane, Walter. *The Decorative Illustration of Books*. London, 1896.

Crow, Gerald H. *William Morris Designer*. London, 1934.

Culot, Jean-Marie. *Bibliographie de Emile Verhaeren*. Brussels, 1954.

Darmstadt, Hessisches Landesmuseum. *Joseph M. Olbrich, 1867-1908, Das Werk des Architekten* [exh. cat.]. Darmstadt, 1967.

Day, Kenneth, ed. *Book Typography 1815-1965 in Europe and the United States of America*. Chicago, 1965.

Delteil, Loÿs. *Le Peintre-Graveur Illustré, XIXe, XXe Siècles*. 31 vols. Paris, 1906-1930.

Denis, Maurice. *Théories, 1890-1910*. Paris, 1920.

Field, Michael, pseud. *Works and Days*. London, 1933.

Garvey, Eleanor M. "Art Nouveau and the French Book of the Eighteen-Nineties," *Harvard Library Bulletin*, XII (1958), 375-391.

Geffroy, Gustave. *René Lalique*. Paris. 1922.

Ghent, Musée des Beaux Arts. *Théo van Rysselberghe*. Exh. cat. by Paul Eeckhout. Ghent, 1962.

Graham, F. Lanier. *Hector Guimard* [exh. cat.]. New York, The Museum of Modern Art, 1970.

Graz, Neue Galerie, Landesmuseum. *Koloman Moser, 1868-1918, Gemaelde, Graphik* [exh. cat.]. Graz, 1969.

Guichard, L. *L'Oeuvre et l'Ame de Jules Renard*. Paris, 1935.

Guignard, Jacques. "Les Livres illustrés de Maurice Denis," *Le Portique*, no. 4 (1946), 49-71.

Gullans, Charles B. and Espey, John J. *A Checklist of Trade Bindings Designed by Margaret Armstrong* (UCLA Library Occasional Papers, No. 16). Los Angeles, University of California Library, 1968.

Hague, Museum Meermanno-Westreenianum. *Het Nederlandse Boek en de Nieuwe Kunst, 1892-1906* [exh. cat.]. Hague, 1965.

Hamburg, Museum für Kunst und Gewerbe. *Plakat-und Buchkunst um 1900* [exh. cat.]. Hamburg, 1963.

Henderson, Philip. *William Morris, his Life, Work and Friends*. New York, 1967.

Hiatt, Charles. "Designs by Will H. Bradley," *The Studio*, IV (1894), 166-168.

Hiatt, Charles. *Picture Posters*. London, 1895.

Hillier, Bevis. *Posters*. New York, 1969.

Hitchcock, Henry-Russell. *In the Nature of Materials: The Buildings of Frank Lloyd Wright*. New York, 1942.

Hofmann, Werner. *Turning Points in Twentieth-Century Art, 1890-1917*. New York, 1969.

Hofstätter, Hans H. *Jugendstil Druckkunst*. Baden-Baden [1968].

Holmes, C. J. *Self & Partners (Mostly Self)*. London [1936].

The Houghton Library. *Vienna, 1888-1939* [exh. cat.]. Cambridge, Mass., 1967.

Housman, Laurence. *The Unexpected Years*. New York [1936].

Howarth, Thomas. *Charles Rennie Mackintosh and the Modern Movement*. [London, 1952].

Hudson, Derek. *Arthur Rackham, his Life and Work. Appendix C: the Printed Work of Arthur Rackham* compiled by Bertram Rota. London [1960].

Hünich, Fritz Adolf. *Rilke-Bibliographie*. Leipzig, 1935.

The Huntington Library, San Marino, California. *Will Bradley, His Work, an Exhibition*. San Marino, 1951.

Jackson, Holbrook. *The Eighteen Nineties*. New York, 1925.

Julien, Edouard. *Les Affiches de Toulouse-Lautrec*. Monte Carlo, 1952.

Jullian, Philippe. *Oscar Wilde*. Violet Wyndham, trans. New York, 1968.

Koch, Robert. "Art Nouveau Bing," *Gazette des Beaux-Arts*, VI per., LIII (1959), 179-190.

Koch, Robert. "Will Bradley," *Art in America*, L (1962), 78-83.

Konody, P. G. *The Art of Walter Crane*. London, 1902.

Kornfeld und Klipstein, Bern. *Jugendstil, Art Nouveau* [Auction cat. #124.]. 22-23 March, 1968.

Lane, Albert. *Elbert Hubbard and his Work*. [Worcester, 1901].

Latimore, Sarah Briggs and Haskell, Grace Clark. *Arthur Rackham, a Bibliography*. Los Angeles, 1936.

Lewis, John. *The Twentieth Century Book, its Illustration and Design* [New York, 1967].

Loubier, Hans. *Die Neue Deutsche Buchkunst*. Stuttgart, 1921.

Louÿs, Pierre. *Journal Intime, 1882-1826*. Paris, 1929.

Madsen, S. Tschudi. *Art Nouveau*. R. I. Christopherson, trans. New York [1967].

McLean, Ruari. *Modern Book Design*. London, 1958.

Mahé, Raymond. *Bibliographie des Livres de Luxe de 1900 à 1928*. 3 vols. Paris, 1931.

Mason, Stuart. *Bibliography of Oscar Wilde, with a note by Robert Ross*. London [1914].

Massé, Gertrude C. E. *A Bibliography of First Editions of Books illustrated by Walter Crane*. London, 1923.

Mellerio, André. *Odilon Redon*. Paris, 1913.

Mont. "Frantz M. Melchers," *The Studio*, XVII (1897), 85-87.

Moore, T. Sturge, intro. by. *Charles Ricketts R. A.; Sixty-five Illustrations*. London [1933].

Mornand, Pierre and Thomé, J.-R. *Vingt Artistes du Livre*. Paris [1950]; p. 57-70, "Maurice Denis."

Mucha, Jiri. *Alphonse Mucha, The Master of Art Nouveau*. Prague, 1966.

Münster, Westfälischer Kunstverein. *Melchior Lechter Gedächtnisausstellung zur hundertsten Wiederkehr seines Geburtstages* [exh. cat.]. Münster, 1965.

Muir, Percy. *Minding my own Business*. London, 1956.

Nebehay, Christian M., ed. *Gustav Klimt Dokumentation*. Vienna, 1969.

Nebehay, Christian M., [Gallery], Vienna. *Gustav Klimt* [exh. cat. no. 33]. Vienna, 1962.

Nebehay, Ingo. "Gerlach's Jugendbücherei," *Das Antiquariat*, Heft 11-12 (1966).

New York, The Museum of Modern Art. *Art Nouveau, Art and Design at the Turn of the Century*. New York [1960].

Orcutt, William Dana. *In Quest of the Perfect Book*. Boston, 1926.

Pennell, E. R. and J. *The Life of James McNeill Whistler*. 2 vols. London, 1908.

Pevsner, Nikolaus. *Pioneers of Modern Design from William Morris to Walter Gropius*. Harmondsworth, Middlesex [1960]. (First pub. 1936 as *Pioneers of the Modern Movement*).

Pissarro, Lucien. *Notes on the Eragny Press, and a letter to J. B. Manson*. Ed. Alan Fern. Cambridge, 1957.

La Plume, no. 197, "Alphonse Mucha et son Oeuvre." Paris, 1897.

The Poster [New York? 1898-1899].

Reade, Brian. *Art Nouveau and Alphonse Mucha*. London, 1967.

Reade, Brian. *Aubrey Beardsley*. New York [1967].

Reade, Brian. *Aubrey Beardsley Picture Book*. London, 1966. (Victoria and Albert Museum Large Picture Book No. 32).

Rewald, John. *Pierre Bonnard*. New York, 1948.

Rheims, Maurice. *The Flowering of Art Nouveau*. New York, 1968.

[Ricketts, Charles]. *A Bibliography of the Books issued by Hacon and Ricketts*. London, 1904.

Ricketts, Charles and Pissarro, Lucien. *De la Typographie et de l'Harmonie de la Page Imprimée* [London, 1898].

Ricketts, Charles. *A Defence of the Revival of Printing* [London, 1899].

Ricketts, Charles. *Self-Portrait, Taken from the Letters & Journals of Charles Ricketts. Collected and compiled by T. Sturge Moore.* Ed. Cecil Lewis. London [1939].

Ritzer, Walter, *Rainer Maria Rilke Bibliographie*. Vienna, 1951.

Robb, Brian. "The Wood-engravings of Lucien Pissarro," *Signature*, n. s. 6 (1948), 36-47.

Ross, Robert. *Aubrey Beardsley*. London and New York, 1909.

Rostand, Edmond. *La Princesse Lointaine*. Trans. into English by Charles Renould. New York, 1899.

Rothenstein, William. *Men and Memories, a History of the Arts 1872-1922*. 2 vols. New York, n.d.

Schauer, Georg Kurt. *Deutsche Buchkunst 1890 bis 1960*. 2 vols. Hamburg, 1963.

Schmutzler, Robert. *Art Nouveau* [New York] 1964.

Seitz, Don C. *Writings by & about James Abbott McNeill Whistler*. Edinburgh, 1910.

Soulier, Gustave. "La Plante et ses Applications Ornementales," *Art et Decoration*, I (1897), 187-189.

Stuck-Villa, Munich. *Jugendstil Illustration in München* [exh. cat.]. Munich, 1969-1970.

"Studio New Publications," *The Studio*, II (1894), 143-146; *The Studio*, IV (1894), xli.

"Studio Reviews of Recent Publications," *The Studio*, IX, (1897), 215-222.

"Studio Talk," *The Studio*, IX (1897), 63-65; *The Studio*, XXIII (1901), 48f.

Symons, A. J. A. "An Unacknowledged Movement in Fine Printing, the Typography of the Eighteen-Nineties," *The Fleuron*, VII (1930), 83-119.

Talvert, Hector and Place, Joseph. *Bibliographie des Auteurs Modernes de Langue Française (1801-1927)*. Paris, 1928.

Taylor, John Russell. *The Art Nouveau Book in Britain* [Cambridge, Mass. 1967.]

Terrasse, Charles. *Bonnard*. Paris, 1927.

Thorpe, James. *English Illustration: the Nineties*. London [1935].

Uzanne, Octave. *L'Art dans la Décoration Extérieure des Livres*. Paris, 1898.

Uzanne, Octave. "Eugène Grasset and Decorative Art in France," *The Studio*, IV (1894), 37-47.

Uzanne, Octave. "On the Drawings of M. Georges de Feure," *The Studio*, XII (1898), 95-102.

Vallance, Aymer. *William Morris, his Art, his Writings, and his Public Life*. London, 1897.

Vienna, Österreichisches Museum für Angewandte Kunst. *Die Wiener Werkstätte, Modernes Kunsthandwerk von 1903-1932* [exh. cat.]. Vienna, 1967.

Vicaire, Georges. *Manuel de l'Amateur de Livres du XIXe Siècle*. 8 vols. Paris, 1894-1920.

Victoria and Albert Museum, London. *Aubrey Beardsley, Exhibition. cat. by Brian Reade and Frank Dickinson*. London, 1966.

Victoria and Albert Museum, London. *Charles Rennie Mackintosh, a Centenary Exhibition*. Cat. by Andrew McLaren Young. London [1968].

Vollmer, Hans. *Allgemeines Lexikon der Bildenden Künstler des XX Jahrhunderts*. 6 vols. Leipzig, 1953.

Waissenberger, Robert. *Buchkunst aus Wien*. Vienna-Munich [1966].

Watkinson, Ray. *William Morris as Designer*. New York, 1967.

Weisberg, Gabriel P. "Samuel Bing, Patron of Art Nouveau," *Connoisseur* (1969), pt. 1: 119-125; pt. 2: 294-299.

White, Gleeson. "The Artistic Decoration of Cloth Book-Covers," *The Studio*, IV (1894), 15-23.

White, Gleeson. "Some Glasgow Designers and Their Work," (Part I), *The Studio*, XI (1897), 86-100.

Wick, Peter and Sessions, Barbara. *Yvette Guilbert*. New York, 1968.

Wien um 1900, Ausstellung Veranstaltet vom Kulturamt der Stadt Wien. Vienna, 1964.

Wilde, Oscar. *Decorative Art in America*. New York, 1906.

Wright, Frank Lloyd. *An Autobiography*. New York, 1943.

Wright Frank Lloyd. *On Architecture*. New York, 1941.

"The Work of Miss Ethel Reed," *The Studio*, X (1897), 230-236.

Zapf, Hermann. *William Morris, sein Leben und Werk in der Geschichte der Buch-und Schriftkunst*. Lübeck, 1949.

Ziff, Larzer. *The American 1890s, Life and Times of a Lost Generation*. New York, 1966.

Zürich, Kunstgewerbemuseum. *Druckkunst des Jugendstils* [exh. cat.]. Zürich, 1966.

Index of Artists

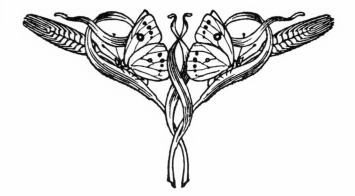

Index of Authors

Index of Publishers

Index of Printers

Index of Vignettes

Numbers in italics refer to catalogue entries

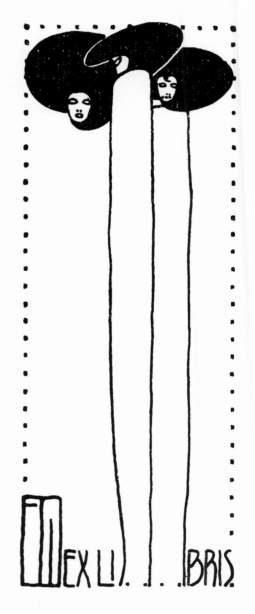

Catalogue by Eleanor M. Garvey,
Anne B. Smith, and Peter A. Wick.
Designed by Larry Webster.
Text type set in Antique #1 with
Bookman Medium Italic phototype
for display sizes.
Printed by
Thomas Todd Company, Boston, on
Mohawk Superfine paper with
Strathmore Rhododendron cover.